Carl Flesch

SCALE SYSTEM

SCALE EXERCISES
in All Major and Minor Keys for Daily Study

A Supplement to Book 1 of
THE ART OF VIOLIN PLAYING

Revised and Enlarged Edition by
MAX ROSTAL

Published jointly by

VERLAG VON RIES & ERLER

Charlottenbrunner Strasse 42
D-14193 Berlin (Grunewald), Germany

and

CARL FISCHER®
65 Bleecker Street, New York, NY 10012

O5188

ISBN 0-8258-0413-2

VORWORT

Ich habe lange gezögert, ehe ich mich dazu entschloß, das in alle Tonarten transponierte *Skalensystem** zu veröffentlichen. Denn bisher bin ich ein Gegner der allzuvielen Ausgaben dieser Art gewesen, die zumeist einander glichen, wie ein Ei dem anderen, und denen nur ganz selten ein origineller Gedanke zugrunde lag.

Im I. Bande meiner „*Kunst des Violinspiels*" hatte ich eine Zusammenstellung von Tonleitern und zerlegten Akkorden veröffentlicht, von denen ich annehmen durfte, daß sie etwas Neues zu bedeuten hatten. Ich versuchte das tägliche Studium der starren Formeln der allgemeinen Technik in geregelte Bahnen zu leiten, den Schüler zu zwingen, nicht die eine Art zugunsten der anderen zu vernachlässigen oder zu bevorzugen, sondern seine Arbeitszeit in gleichmäßiger Weise auf die gebräuchlichsten technischen Kombinationen zu verteilen, während ich in rein formaler Hinsicht die der altfranzösischen Schule geläufige Art der Tonleitersequenzen in Doppelgriffen der heutigen Generation wieder ins Gedächtnis zurückrief. Jahrelange Praxis hat in mir die Überzeugung gefestigt, daß das „*Skalensystem*" infolge seiner Universalität und Gedrängtheit sowohl das erfolgreichste als auch das zeit- und kraftsparendste Übungsverfahren auf dem Gebiete der allgemeinen Technik darstellt — allerdings unter einer bestimmten Voraussetzung: *daß nämlich der Übende jeden Tag die Tonleiter wechselt, d. h. den Grundtypus nach und nach in alle Tonarten transponiert.* Infolge Raummangels sah ich mich jedoch im I. Bande der „Kunst des Violinspiels" genötigt, bloß das Skalensystem in C-Dur im Sinne eines Musters zu veröffentlichen und es dem

---

* Auch den Ausdruck „System" gebrauche ich nur der Not gehorchend, weil mir eben keine prägnantere Bezeichnung in den Sinn kam. Ich beabsichtige damit bloß die festgefügte praktisch-erprobte F o r m, jedoch nicht eine starre unelastische Übungsart zu bezeichnen, die dem Wesen echter künstlerischer Freiheit stets entgegengesetzt ist. In der Kunst ist bloß ein einziges System gestattet: *Systemlosigkeit.*

PREFACE

I hesitated considerably before deciding upon publication of the *Scalesystem** transposed to all keys, because thus far I have been opposed to the superabundance of editions devoted to material of this order, which were rarely based upon any original idea, and generally as alike as two peas.

In Book One of my *"Art of Violin Playing"* I had presented a compilation of Scales and Broken Chords under the heading, "The System of Scales", which I was prepared to believe was a significant innovation. I endeavored to conduct the daily study of rigid, general technical formulas along regulated systematic paths, in order to prevent the pupil from favoring one variety in preference to another, in other words, to compel him to divide his study period equally between the usual and most necessary technical combinations. A second consideration was to bring to the attention of our present generation the fluent methods of the classic French school for the playing of scale sequences in double stops.

Long years of practical experience have strengthened my conviction that the System of Scales, in consequence of its universal and concise form provides a method of practice, beneficial not only for technical development in general but also for the saving of considerable time — this, however, with a decided proviso — *that the student will change the scale every day, and in this way gradually transpose the fundamental type into all keys.* Owing to lack of space, however, I was obliged to publish the System of Scales only in C Major (in form of a model) and leave it to the student to do the transposing himself.

Three years have now passed since original publication of Book I. of

---

* I am using here the word "System" in want of a better one and against my inclination. It is merely meant to denote a practically tested form and not by any means a rigid unelastic method of practising, which is always inimical to genuine artistic delivery. The prerequisite of true artistry is the entire freedom from all and every kind of "Systems".

PREFACE

J'ai longtemps hésité avant de me décider à publier mon *système* de gammes* transposé dans toutes les tonalités. Car je n'ai jamais incliné en faveur des publications trop nombreuses de ce genre. D'habitude elles se ressemblent a s'y méprendre, sans se distinguer entre elles par une idée nouvelle, laquelle devrait constituer leur seule raison d'être.

Dans le Iᵉʳ volume de mon *«Art du Violon»* j'avais publié une suite de gammes et d'accords brisés, dont je pouvais admettre avec une certaine raison qu'elle signifiait quelque chose de nouveau. J'avais essayé de diriger le travail journalier des formules de la technique générale dans une voie qui ne permettait pas à l'élève de favoriser une partie du mécanisme au détriment d'une autre, mais qui l'obligerait à diviser son travail d'une façon égale entre les combinaisons techniques les plus en usage. D'autre part j'ai taché de ressusciter la manière dont la vieille école française avait l'habitude de faire travailler les gammes, une tradition que j'avais recueilli en ligne droite chez mon ancien professeur *Eugène Sauzay,* gendre de *Baillot.* Une pratique de longues années avait fortifié en moi la conviction, que grâce à son universalité et à sa concision, ce système de gammes ne constituait non seulement une garantie sure de progrès continu, mais qu'il représentait en même temps le meilleur moyen d'économiser aussi bien son temps que ses forces. Pour arriver à ce resultat enviable il fallait cependant que l'élève changeât chaque jour la tonalité en transposant successivement le modèle primitif d'ut-majeur dans tous les autres tons. Je m'étais vu forcé par manque de place de ne publier dans la première partie de *«l'Art du Violon»* que le dit

---

* Je me sers du mot *«système»* uniquement par nécessité et non par sympathie. Par lui je ne veux désigner qu'une forme concentrée à l'extrême et non une manière d'étudier, inexorablement raide et engourdie. En art le seul système permis consiste à ne pas en avoir.

Übenden zu überlassen, die Transpositionen vorzunehmen.

Es sind nun 3 Jahre verflossen, seit der I. Band meines Werkes in deutscher Sprache und 1—2 Jahre, seit er in englischer, holländischer und italienischer Sprache erschienen ist (die französische Ausgabe befindet sich im Druck.) Ich habe während dieser Zeit zur Genüge Gelegenheit gehabt, die Auswirkungen des Skalensystems zu beurteilen, und es bedeutete eine gewisse Enttäuschung für mich, teils aus eigener Anschauung, teils aus fremden Berichten feststellen zu müssen, daß die Mehrzahl der Übenden die Mühen der Transposition scheute und sich damit begnügte, das Skalensystem ausschließlich in C=Dur zu spielen. Es liegt auf der Hand, daß durch diese Beschränkung auf eine einzige Tonart der praktische Nutzen meines Systems erheblich vermindert wird, und daß der Geiger, der sich daran gewöhnt, Tonleitern in 24 Tonarten zu üben, vor dem anderen, der sich ausschließlich auf C=Dur konzentriert, einen beträchtlichen Vorsprung hat. Ich habe mich daher, vielfachen Aufforderungen nachgebend und mein ursprüngliches Widerstreben bezwingend, dazu entschlossen, zu Nutz und Frommen der jungen und vielleicht auch einiger älterer Geiger das vollständige Skalensystem in allen 24 Tonarten zu veröffentlichen.

Zur Ausführung der Übungen wäre noch folgendes zu bemerken:

1. Das Skalensystem stellt entweder eine Intonationsübung oder eine Geläufigkeitsübung dar. Im erstern Falle wird es *langsam* unter Verbesserung aller falschen Töne, im zweiten Falle *rasch* geübt.

2. *Die Tonart muß jeden Tag gewechselt werden.*

3 Ich habe es vorgezogen, die Skalen in *Doppelgriffen* in den *Moll*tonarten *harmonisch* statt melodisch zu gestalten, weil diese Art infolge der übermäßigen Sekundengriffe meist vernachlässigt wird. Die *einfachen* Molltonleitern habe ich hingegen *melodisch* notiert, während die Folgen in gebrochenen Terzen beide Arten vereinigen.

my Work in German, and one to two years since its appearance in English, Dutch and Italian (a French edition is in press). During this time I have had plentiful opportunity to judge of the practical usefulness of the System of Scales, and guided by my own observations, as well as reports from other quarters, I must admit (not without a certain amount of personal disappointment) that the majority of students shunned the extra exertion of tranposition and were satisfied to practice the System of Scales exclusively in C Major. It may readily be understood that through the limitation of one key, the practical usefulness of such daily studies is considerably diminished, and that any violinist, accustomed to practizing the scales in twenty=four keys, will have a decided advantage over the other, who concentrates exclusively upon C=Major. Therefore, yielding to numerous requests and overcoming my original opposition, I decided to publish the Scalesystem in all twenty=four keys for the benefit of younger—and possibly some of the older—violinists as well.

In relation to executing the studies the following is to be observed:

I. The System of Scales provides exercises equally serviceable for intonation and facility. In the former case it is practiced *slowly,* to allow of perfecting the intonation, in the latter case, *rapidly.*

II. *The key must be changed every day.*

III. For the Minor Key Scales in Double Stops, I have preferred the *Harmonic* to the *Melodic* form, as this variety, owing to the augmented seconds, is neglected as a rule. The simple Minor scales on the other hand have been added in *Melodic* form, while both varieties have been combined in the Scales in broken Thirds.

modèle en ut=majeur en laissant aux élèves le soin des transpositions.

Trois ans se sont écoulés depuis la publication du Ier volume de mon ouvrage. Depuis j'ai eu l'occasion d'observer l'influence du système de gammes sur les élèves. J'avoue que ce fut pour moi une certaine déception, de constater à la suite de mes propres observations ou d'après celles des autres, que la plupart des élèves avait reculé devant la difficulté des transpositions et s'était contentée à travailler les gammes en ut=majeur. L'effet positif s'en trouvait sensiblement diminué. Il est tout naturel que le violiniste qui s'habitue à exercer les gammes dans tous les tons possède un grand avantage sur celui qui se contente d'une seule tonalité, toujours la même. Voilà la raison qui m'a décidé à surmonter ma propre résistance, ainsi qu'à céder aux sollicitations des autres en publiant le système complet des gammes.

Voici quelques observations utiles pour la mise en pratique des exercices:

I° Le système de gammes peut servir aussi bien comme exercice d'intonation que comme exercice de vélocité. Dans le premier cas il doit être joué *lentement* en corrigeant chaque fausse note, dans le second cas une vitesse, appropriée au mécanisme individuel, est de mise.

II° *La tonalité doit être changée tous les jours.*

III° Les gammes mineures en *doubles cordes* sont écrites dans le mode *harmonique* et non *mélodique,* pour faire usage des intervalles de secondes augmentées que l'on néglige généralement. J'ai donné par contre aux gammes mineures *simples* la forme mélodique, tandis que les gammes en tierces brisées réunissent les deux manières.

4. Um die für das Skalensystem zur Verfügung stehende Zeit aufs äußerste auszunutzen, habe ich die einfachen Tonleitern mit Bogenstrichübungen verbunden. Dieselben können auch in den Doppelgriffkombinationen in gleicher Weise angewandt werden, sofern diese, statt zusammenklingend, gebrochen gespielt werden, z. B.:

IV. In order to use the time at one's disposal for the System of Scales to utmost advantage, I have combined the simple scales with bowing exercises. The same may also be used in like manner for the double-stop combinations, in such cases where the intervals are not sounded simultaneously, but broken, for instance:

IV° Afin d'utiliser autant que possible le temps disponible, j'ai greffé des exercices d'archet sur les gammes. Ces coups d'archet peuvent aussi s'appliquer aux exercices en doubles cordes, si l'on prend soin de les briser. Par exemple:

5. Es bleibt dem Übenden überlassen, die Tonleitern und Akkordfolgen mit verschiedenen dynamischen Nuancen zu versehen:

V. It is left to the student to add various nuances to the scales and chord progressions, as follows:

V° L'élève peut ajouter à volonté certaines nuances dynamiques:

6. Am Schluß einer jeden Tonleiterreihe habe ich einige Übungen in einfachen Flageolettönen, sowie mehrere Doppelflageoletts hinzugefügt, weil nach meiner Erfahrung viele Geiger dieses technische Gebiet vernachlässigen und in große Verlegenheit kommen, wenn ihr Repertoire sie zufällig zwingt, sich der Flageoletts zu bedienen.

VI. At the end of each scale succession, I have added a few exercises in single and several in double-stop harmonics, for the reason, that many violinists neglect this form of technic and are likely to be embarrassed, if their repertoire should by chance force them to employ harmonics.

VI° J'ai cru utile de finir chaque série par des exercices en *harmoniques* simples et doubles, puisque l'on s'occupe trop rarement de cette spécialité, ce qui fait, que la plupart des violonistes se trouvent fort embarassés lorsque leur répertoire les oblige à s'en servir.

7. Um das Notenbild dieser fünfsprachigen Ausgabe nicht übermäßig zu belasten, habe ich die Strichart bloß mittels Abkürzungen in deutscher Sprache angegeben. Demnach bedeutet Sp. = *Spitze*, M. = *Mitte*, Fr. = *Frosch*, G. B. = *ganzer Bogen*, H. B. = *halber Bogen*, die Ausdrücke *Martelé* sowie *Spiccato* sind wohl den Geigern aller Länder geläufig.

VII. In order not to crowd the printed pages of this edition now appearing in five languages, to too great an extent, I have indicated the bowings only in German, in abbreviated form. Consequently, Sp. means *tip of bow*, M. = *middle*, Fr. = *nut*, G.B. = *whole bow*, H.B. = *half bow*, *Martelé*, as well as *Spiccato* are almost identical in sound in all the languages.

VII° Afin de ne pas surcharger le texte de cette édition publiée en cinq langues je me suis servi pour l'indication des coups d'archets d'abréviations en langue allemande. Leur signification est la suivante: Sp.=*pointe*, M. = *milieu*; Fr. = *talon*; G. B. = *tout l'archet*; H. B. = *moitié de l'archet*. *Martelé* et *Spiccato* signifient dans toutes les langues à peu près la même chose.

8. Die von *Ševčik* in seiner Schule des Violinspiels eingeführte Reihenfolge zerlegter Akkorde habe ich auch im Skalensystem als die zweckmäßigste Zusammenstellung beibehalten.

VIII. The succession of broken chords as introduced by *Ševčik* in his Violin Method has also been retained by me in the System of Scales as the most practical compilation.

VIII° L'ordre dans lequel, les accords brisés se suivent est le même que celui dont *Ševčik* se sert dans son Ecole du Mécanisme du Violon.

Bei der Abfassung dieser Arbeit ist mir Herr Alfred *Fink* aus *Straßburg* in hervorragender Weise behilflich gewesen, wofür ihm mein besonderer Dank gebührt.

The valuable assistance rendered by Mr. Alfred *Fink* of *Strassburg*, in the preparation of this work, is herewith gratefully acknowledged.

Je dois remercier sincèrement M. *Alfred Fink* de *Strasbourg* pour son précieux appui durant les préparatifs de publication de cet ouvrage.

Vorwort des Herausgebers der Neuausgabe

Anlaß zur Neubearbeitung des seit vielen Jahren bewährten Skalensystems von Carl Flesch ist die Tatsache, daß seine Entstehung etwa 60 Jahre zurückliegt. Die in dem Skalensystem dargestellten Grundlagen haben zwar nach wie vor ihre Gültigkeit, doch hat sich in den vergangenen sechs Jahrzehnten eine so rasante Entwicklung vollzogen, daß das zur Zeit erreichte Niveau des Geigens neue Anforderungen stellt, die zu vervollständigen ich mir zur Aufgabe gemacht habe, so z. B. durch das Hinzufügen unserem Zeitgeschmack entsprechender Fingersätze, die sich aber deutlich von den originalen Flesch-Fingersätzen unterscheiden, indem sich diese nun ausschließlich über den Noten befinden und meine Vorschläge unter den Noten. Die alternativen Fingersätze von Flesch bleiben ebenfalls über den Noten in runden Klammern ( ) erhalten. Es war mir ein Bedürfnis, den Flesch-Text sozusagen als Urtext zu erhalten, um so dem jeweiligen Lehrer oder auch dem Übenden die Wahl zu überlassen.

Manche Fingersätze von Flesch werden gelegentlich mißverstanden, daher füge ich außer meinen eigenen Fingersätzen sozusagen erläuternde Ergänzungen bei.

Die von mir stammenden Fingersätze sind nicht als „Verbesserungen" zu verstehen; sie stellen dem heutigen Geschmack entsprechende Alternativen dar, so daß abwechselnd beide Fingersätze, die von Flesch und die meinigen, geübt werden können. Die Ansicht vieler Lehrer, möglichst uniformierte Fingersätze für alle Tonarten anzuwenden, teile ich nicht, schon weil aus musikalischen Gründen oft entsprechend sinnvolle Fingersätze Anwendung finden sollten.

Ich verwende also oft erleichternde, aber auch manchmal absichtlich schwerere Fingersätze, um so auch für musikalisch oder technisch bedingte Ausnahmen gewappnet zu sein. Die an ähnlichen Stellen nicht konsequent durchgeführten Fingersätze entsprechen also der Absicht, Erfahrungen verschiedenster Art zu trainieren. So manche, fast pendantische Übergenauigkeit der Fingersatzangaben sind für den noch nicht eingeweihten Schüler gedacht. Wenn nichts anderes notiert, gelten auch für mich die Fingersätze von Flesch.

Leider werden meine Fingersätze öfters nicht wirklich verstanden und erscheinen so manchem „routinierten Veteranen" als absurd. Für mich ist es ganz klar, daß die leichteren Fingersätze nicht immer auch die musikalischsten und sinnvollsten sind. Wenn man bereit ist, künstlerische Ideen aus Gründen der Sicherheit zu opfern, kann das Violinspiel beträchtlich erleichtert werden. Die nicht sofort einleuchtenden Fingersätze werden meistens nicht nach Gründen und Ursachen untersucht. Fallen sie nicht in die bekannten Klischees und Schablonen, werden sie allzu leichtfertig als „unspielbar oder unsicher", manchmal sogar als „verrückt" erklärt. Aber der Fingersatz auf einem Streichinstrument ist mehr als ein

Editor's Preface to the New Edition

The present edition of Carl Flesch's Scale System is based on the well-proven original which appeared some sixty years ago. Although the fundamental ideas conveyed in the Scale System are still valid, violin playing has undergone such rapid development over the past six decades that I felt the need to respond to the new demands of the standards it has attained today. Thus I have added fingerings in keeping with current taste, distinguishing them clearly from Flesch's original fingerings by placing his above the notes while my own suggestions are printed below the notes. Flesch's alternative fingerings, enclosed in parentheses, also remain above the notes. It was my desire to preserve Flesch's version as the original text as it were, leaving the teacher or student free to choose between the alternatives.

Apart from my own fingering suggestions, I have also added explanations about Flesch's fingerings, some of which are occasionally misunderstood.

The fingerings I have supplied are not to be seen as "improvements" but rather as alternatives representing present-day taste; both types of fingering, Flesch's and mine, may be practised. I do not share the opinion of numerous teachers that all keys should be fingered in a uniformed way, particularly for musical reasons, which require often different and appropriate fingerings.

In many cases I have used fingerings that facilitate execution of a given passage, but sometimes the fingerings have been deliberately made difficult in order to prepare the student for the exceptions that arise for musical or technical reasons. Seemingly inconsistent fingerings for similar passages have been suggested with the intention of acquainting the students with musical and technical exceptions. Numerous, almost pedantic fingerings are meant for the as yet uninitiated student. If not otherwise indicated, the fingerings of Flesch are to be applied.

Unfortunately, my fingerings are occasionally not really understood and may seem absurd to many "experienced veterans". It is quite clear to me that easier fingerings are not always the most musical and significant ones. If one is prepared to sacrifice artistic concepts for safety, playing the violin can be greatly facilitated. Fingerings that are not immediately comprehensible are usually not examined for underlying reasons and motives. If the suggestions do not agree with the known clichées and patterns, they are too rashly declared to be "unplayable or unsafe", sometimes even "crazy". But fingerings on a string instrument are more than a practical means of alleviating difficulties. They are, or should be, an important part of the art of interpretation, and if at times technical complications ensue, it is desirable to raise the player's technical level to meat those high demands. Excessive willingness to compromise may result in a lack of responsibility. As to the additions that I regard as important, I wish to make the

Préface de l'éditeur de la réédition

La motivation pour cette nouvelle édition refondue du système de gammes de Carl Flesch – ayant fait ses preuves depuis de nombreuses années – émane du fait que son origine date de soixante ans en arrière. Bien que les principes fondamentaux de ce système soient toujours valables, j'ai tenu compte du développement rapide qui s'est produit pendant ces six décennies passées. Le niveau actuel du jeu de violon comprend de nouvelles exigences et je considère comme ma tâche d'y répondre, p. ex. en ajoutant des doigtés correspondant au goût actuel. Mes propositions de doigtés qui se distinguent clairement de ceux de Flesch sont placés sous les notes, tandis que ceux de Flesch se trouvent exclusivement sur les notes. Les alternatives proposées par Flesch sont mises entre parenthèses ( ), également au-dessus des notes. Je tenais à conserver le texte original de Flesch tel quel afin que les utilisateurs de ce livre, professeurs et élèves aient le choix.

Certains doigtés de Flesch risquent d'être mal interprétés. Pour cette raison, j'ajoute outre mes propres propositions des suppléments explicatifs.

Je ne considère pas mes doigtés comme des «corrections»; ils représentent plutôt des alternatives qui correspondent au goût de nos jours et ils peuvent être joués en alternance avec ceux de Flesch. Je ne partage pas l'avis d'un grand nombre d'enseignants qui emploient, dans la mesure du possible, des doigtés uniformes dans toutes les tonalités, car pour des raisons musicales, je crois nécessaire de choisir des doigtés adéquats.

J'utilise donc souvent des doigtés qui facilitent le jeu, mais, de temps à autre, aussi, et sciemment, des doigtés plus difficiles afin que les violonistes soient à même de maîtriser des exceptions sur le plan musical ou technique. Le fait que des passages qui se ressemblent sont doigtés de façon différente émane de mon intention de faire exercer des expériences les plus diverses. La précision quelquefois méticuleuse des doigtés s'adresse aux élèves non initiés. A moins qu'il n'en soit noté autrement, les doigtés de Flesch sont valables aussi pour moi.

Je regrette que, à l'occasion, mes doigtés ne soient pas réellement compris et paraissent à certains vieux routiniers même absurdes. Pour moi, il est évident que les doigtés les plus faciles ne sont pas toujours aussi les plus musicaux et les plus judicieux. Si l'on accepte que l'idée artistique est subordonnée à la sécurité de l'exécution, la pratique du violon devient beaucoup plus facile. Dans la plupart des cas, on n'étudie pas les raisons des doigtés inintelligibles de prime abord. Si ceux-ci ne correspondent pas aux stéréotypes et formules connus, on les déclare, trop vite et à la légère, «injouables et risqués», et quelquefois même «fous». Mais sur un instrument à cordes le doigté est plus qu'un moyen pratique d'éviter des difficultés. Il est ou devrait être une partie importante de l'art

praktisches Mittel, Schwierigkeiten zu erleichtern. Er ist oder sollte ein ganz wichtiger Teil der Interpretationskunst sein, und wenn sich daraus hier und da technische Erschwerungen ergeben, wäre es wünschenswert, das technische Niveau diesen Anforderungen anzugleichen. Eine zu weitgehende Kompromißbereitschaft kann zur Verantwortungslosigkeit führen.

Zu den mir wichtig erscheinenden Hinzufügungen sei erwähnt, daß ich außer den von Flesch vorgeschlagenen Serpentinen auch geradlinige Skalen anwende und gelegentlich die Tonleiter auf je einer Saite in nur einer Oktave auf zwei Oktaven ausdehne, ebenfalls die dreioktavigen Skalen öfters auf vier Oktaven erweitere. Moll-Tonarten werden in meiner Version getrennt harmonisch und melodisch behandelt. In Doppelgriffen füge ich die bei Flesch noch nicht vorhandenen Intervalle an, so z.B. Primen, Quarten, Quinten und Septimen; in Sexten, Oktaven und Dezimen weitere Ergänzungen; in Flageoletts, abgesehen vom Normalgriff in der Quartlage, auch mit Fingersätzen, die den Fingersatzoktaven ähnlich sind, Quintengriffe, kleine und große Terzengriffe als notwendige Vorbereitung für Doppelflageoletts; dann die im 20. Jahrhundert angewandten Ganztonleitern und schließlich auch Viertelton-Skalen. Zur linken-Hand-Technik gehören auch Pizzicati, die fast niemals geübt werden.

Nun einige Bemerkungen zum Vorwort von Carl Flesch

„Zur Ausführung der Übungen" schreibt Flesch:

1. „Das Skalensystem' stellt entweder eine Intonationsübung oder eine Geläufigkeitsübung dar. Im ersten Falle wird es langsam unter Verbesserung aller falschen Töne, im zweiten Falle rasch geübt." In Erweiterung dieser Gedanken schlage ich vor, außer der von Flesch erwähnten Intonations- und Geläufigkeitsübung, die Skalen noch überdies als Lagenwechsel- und in einem späteren Stadium als Vibratoübung anzuwenden. Hierzu allerdings noch einige Erläuterungen: bei der Intonationsübung sollte man sich nicht ausschließlich mit der „Verbesserung aller falschen Töne" begnügen, sondern den Zugang zu der falsch befundenen Note erarbeiten, so daß der Ton selbst einwandfrei und ohne die Notwendigkeit der (meist hörbaren) Verbesserung erreicht wird. Die Perfektion auch bei der Distanzmessung im Lagenwechsel wird dadurch trainiert, d.h. immer die Note vor dem nicht gut befundenen Ton als Startpunkt benutzen. Als Lagenwechselübung ist die Unhörbarkeit im Gegensatz zu einem beabsichtigten Espressivo-Glissando zu erarbeiten. Ein – wenn auch nicht ausschließliches – Mittel ist, den Lagenwechsel so oft wie möglich wegen der kürzeren Distanz in ein Halbtonintervall zu legen. Auch die Daumenvorbereitung hat hierbei eine gewissen Anteil. Was nun meinen Vorschlag betrifft, auch das Vibrato einzubeziehen, ist das Üben mit Vibrato erst dann zu empfehlen, wenn die

following comments: apart from the passages proposed by Flesch in a serpentine form, I also use straightlined scales, occasionally extending the scale to be played on each string from one octave to two octaves and the three-octave scales to four octaves. In my version the harmonic and melodic forms of minor keys are dealt with separately. As regards double stops, I have added intervals not yet present in Flesch's work, including unisons, fourths, fifths, sevenths and I also expanded the treatment of sixths, octaves, and tenths. As for harmonics, apart from those played in the normal way with the 1st and 4th finger. I also include fingerings, similar to fingered octaves, as well as fifths, and minor and major thirds, as necessary preparation for double harmonics. Wholetone scales and quarter-tone scales which are used in the twentieth century, have been added. Left-hand technique includes also pizzicati, which are hardly ever practised.

A few comments about the Carl Flesch preface

On the "Execution of the Studies", Flesch notes:

I. "The Scale System provides exercises equally serviceable for intonation and facility. In the former case it is practised slowly, to allow of perfecting the intonation, in the latter case, rapidly." In addition to this concept, I propose that scales be practised not only as intonation and facility exercises mentioned by Flesch but also as an exercise for shifting and, at a later stage, as a vibrato exercise. To this, however, a few explanations may be added: the aim of intonation exercises should not exclusively consist of correcting all false notes, but to work on the access to the wrong note in order to produce it clearly without the necessity of further (and usually audible) adjustement. Thus in shifting the distance measuring is trained more adequately as well; that is, the exercise is to begin every time with the note preceding the faulty one. As a shifting exercise, inaudibility is to be developed as opposed to a deliberate espressivo-glissando. One – though not the exclusive – means to achieve this, is to execute the shift as often as possible between two notes that are only a semitone apart because of the shorter distance involved. Preparatory thumb movements have a certain part in this as well. As to my proposal to include vibrato, it is advisable to practise with vibrato only once the worst intonation problems have been overcome. Practising invariably without vibrato, as so many teachers recommend for

d'interprétation et s'il en résulte parfois des difficultés techniques, il serait souhaitable d'adapter le niveau technique à ces exigences. La disposition trop grande à faire des compromis mène finalement à l'irresponsabilité.

Dans les suppléments, que je crois importants, j'applique, outre les passages en forme serpentine proposés par Flesch, des gammes rectilignes et j'étends quelquefois les gammes comprenant une octave sur la même corde à deux octaves et plus souvent celles de trois octaves à quatre octaves. Dans ma version, les gammes mineures, harmonique et mélodique sont traitées séparément. Pour les exercices en double cordes, j'ajoute les intervalles non traités par Flesch, tels que les unissons, les quartes, quintes et septièmes; je joins pour les sextes d'autres extensions, pour les octaves et dixièmes des extensions; pour les harmoniques, je propose outre le doigté normal de quarte, les doigtés correspondant à ceux des octaves doigtées, les quintes, les tierces mineures et majeures en tant que préparation indispensable aux harmoniques doubles. J'ajoute également les gammes de six tons, dont on use au 20ᵉ siècle, et enfin des gammes en quarts de ton. Font aussi partie de la technique de la main gauche les pizzicati, qui sont presque toujours négligés.

Quelques remarques à la préface de Carl Flesch

Pour «la mise en pratique des exercices» Flesch signale:

Iᵒ «Le système de gammes peut servir aussi bien comme exercice d'intonation que comme exercice de vélocité. Dans le premier cas il doit être joué lentement en corrigeant chaque fausse note, dans le second cas une vitesse appropriée au mécanisme individuel, est de mise.» Pour développer ces idées, je propose d'appliquer les gammes non seulement aux exercices d'intonation et de vélocité, comme Flesch suggère, mais aussi à l'entraînement des changements de position et, plus tard, du vibrato. Dans ce contexte, quelques explications: dans les exercices d'intonation, il ne suffit pas de «corriger chaque fausse note». Il est plutôt nécessaire de travailler l'approche de la note que l'on reconnaît fausse afin de réussir, d'un coup sûr, le ton juste sans correction ultérieure, qui est presque toujours audible. De cette manière, on améliore en même temps l'évaluation des distances lors des changements de position. Comme point de départ on prendra toujours le ton qui se trouve devant le ton reconnu faux. Dans les exercices de changements de position, il faut entraîner le passage inaudible contrairement à l'espressivo-glissando intentionnel. Une méthode, mais non pas la seule, pour y arriver, est de faire le changement de position de préférence dans un intervalle de demi-ton, à cause de la distance raccourcie. La préparation du pouce y joue aussi un certain rôle. Si je suggère d'inclure aussi l'entraînement du

gröberen Intonationsfehler überwunden sind. Das von vielen Lehrern aus Gründen der Intonation empfohlene stets vibratolose Üben ist meines Erachtens eine überholte Ansicht, denn schließlich muß man auch bei Benutzung des Vibratos intonationssicher sein. Im praktischen Spiel benutzt man heutzutage Vibrato aus Gründen der Tonschönheit, der Intensität und zum allgemeinen Ausdrucksvermögen in variabler Form. Es soll also nicht eine Vibratoübung an sich sein, sondern die Bestrebung, unbeabsichtigte Vibratounterbrechungen zu überwinden. Allzu oft wird die Linie einer Folge von gleichklingenden Noten unbewußt und unkontrolliert unterbrochen, was meistens bei letzten Noten vor einem Lagenwechsel und speziell bei Benutzung des 4. Fingers eintritt. Dieser plötzliche Stillstand des Vibratos geschieht nicht aus beabsichtigten künstlerischen und interpretativen Gründen, sondern aus Bequemlichkeit und Nachlässigkeit. Das Trainieren der nicht unterbrochenen Vibratokontinuität als Kette gleichklingender Töne ist in diesem Fall mein Ziel, was keineswegs bedeutet, daß man immer nur die gleiche Art des Vibratos anwenden soll.

2. Bei Flesch: „Die Tonart muß jeden Tag gewechselt werden". Dies sollte zwar Endziel sein, doch kann man das nur erwarten, wenn alle ursprünglichen Schwierigkeiten überwunden sind, sozusagen als Erhaltung und nicht zur Erlernung der Technik. Anfänglich sollte also allerhöchstens zweimal pro Woche die Tonart gewechselt werden, mit späterem Übergang zum Wechsel an jedem zweiten Tag vor dem von Flesch empfohlenen täglichen Wechsel. Das bezieht sich allerdings nur auf die alte, ursprüngliche, unveränderte und nicht revidierte Ausgabe. (Vergleiche Nr. 6 der Übungsmethoden für das Skalensystem.)

3. Die von Flesch angewandte Methode sowohl bei homophonen Molltonarten wie auch bei Doppelgriffen zum Teil melodisch und zum Teil harmonisch zu verfahren, hat in so manchen Fällen zu Verwirrungen geführt. Wahrscheinlich war der Beweggrund dafür, dem Übenden Zeit zu ersparen. Nach meiner Erfahrung werden klare Vorstellungen nur durch strikte Trennung von melodischen und harmonischen Molltonarten erzielt. Zu diesem Passus verweise ich auf meine Bemerkungen im separaten Anhang Seite 126, bevor die angeführten Beispiele in Molltonarten beginnen.

4. Vor Anwendung der von Flesch empfohlenen gleichzeitigen Bogenübungen verwende man anfänglich ausschließlich Bindungen, um die Schwierigkeiten der linken Hand zunächst einmal von der rechten Hand zu trennen. Jede technische Schwierigkeit sollte schließlich zuerst isoliert angegangen werden, bevor man zur Kombination schreitet, was jedenfalls auf einen viel späteren Zeitpunkt verschoben werden sollte. Das Skalensystem dient in erster Linie der linken-Hand-Technik, und gerade das Legatospiel macht den möglichst unhörbaren Lagen- und Saitenwechsel kontrollfähig.

reasons of intonation, is an outdated method in my opinion. After all, even when vibrato is used, intonation must be accurate. When actually making music, string players today use vibrato to enhance tonal beauty, intensity, and general expressiveness in various ways. This is not meant to be a vibrato exercise for its own sake but rather an attempt to overcome unintentional interruptions of vibrato. Too often, the musical line of similar sounding notes is unconsciously interrupted in an uncontrolled fashion. This usually occurs with the note preceding a shift and particularly when the fourth finger is used. This sudden stoppage in the vibrato does not occur out of intended artistic and interpretative reasons but rather out of convenience and negligence. My purpose in this case is to train the execution of vibrato continuity as a sequence of equal sounding tones, which by no means implies using the same kind of vibrato over and over again.

II. Flesch observes that "the key must be changed every day." This indeed should be the final goal, but it can be expected only when all initial difficulties have been mastered, as a means of preserving technique rather than acquire it. At the beginning therefore, the key should be changed twice a week at the very most. Later, it can be changed every other day before one proceeds to the daily change recommended by Flesch. This of course holds good only for the old original and unaltered edition. (Compare Number 6 of Section "Methods of Practising the Scale System.")

III. Flesch's method of switching between harmonic and melodic scales when dealing with homophonic minor keys and double stops has in some cases lead to confusion. His motive probably was to save the student time. In my experience clarity is achieved only by strictly separating melodic and harmonic keys in minor scales. See my remarks in the appendix on page 126 preceding the given examples in minor keys.

IV. Before beginning with the simultaneous bowing exercises recommended by Flesch, the student should at first concentrate on using slurs so as to work on the difficulties of the left hand separately from those of the right. Technical difficulties should in any case be practised in isolation before the student attempts combinations, which be postponed to a much later time. The scale system serves primarily to develop left-hand technique, and legato playing is precisely what allows the inaudible shift and string-crossing to be controllable.

vibrato je ne recommande de le faire que dans la phase où il n'y aura plus de grosses fautes d'intonation. Le refus général du vibrato pour les exercices, préconisé pour des raisons d'intonation par beaucoup d'enseignants, est dépassé, à mon avis, car l'intonation doit être juste et sûre aussi quand on joue vibrato. De nos jours, on se sert du vibrato, en pratique, pour varier la beauté tonale, l'intensité et l'expressivité générale. Il ne s'agit donc pas de s'exercer au vibrato même, mais de surmonter les interruptions du vibrato non intentionnelles et non contrôlées. Trop souvent, la suite des tons égaux est interrompue inconsciemment et de façon non contrôlée surtout aux dernières notes avant un changement de position et, tout particulièrement, si l'on se sert du 4e doigt. Cet arrêt soudain du vibrato est dû non à des raisons artistiques ou interprétatives mais à une certaine paresse et négligence. Il est vrai que, dans ce cas, l'exercice du vibrato continu et ininterrompu est mon objectif, mais cela signifie nullement, qu'il faut toujours appliquer la même sorte de vibrato.

II° Flesch dit: «La tonalité doit être changée chaque jour.» Mais c'est le but final que l'on n'atteindra pas avant que toutes les difficultés initiales soient surmontées, dans une phase donc où il ne s'agit plus d'apprendre la technique mais de la maintenir. D'abord on doit changer la tonalité tout au plus deux fois par semaine, plus tard, tous les deux jours avant de passer au changement quotidien recommandé par Flesch. (Comparez numéro 6 de la rubrique «Méthodes d'entrainement pour le système de gammes.»)

III° La méthode adoptée par Flesch d'alterner aussi bien dans les gammes homophones que dans les doubles cordes, le mineur harmonique et mélodique a abouti à certaines confusions. Probablement le désir d'économiser le temps de l'élève était à l'origine de cette idée. D'après mon expérience, on acquiert, dans les tonalités mineures, des conceptions claires uniquement par une stricte séparation entre mélodique et harmonique. Dans ce contexte, je renvoie à mes notes dans l'appendice p. 126, précédant les exemples que je donne pour les gammes mineures.

IV° Avant de se mettre simultanément aux exercices d'archet, je recommande de jouer, pour un certain temps, exclusivement des notes liées pour détacher les difficultés de la main gauche de celles de la main droite. Il faut, en effet, commencer par aborder isolément chaque difficulté technique, avant d'en combiner plusieurs, bien sûr beaucoup plus tard. Le système de gammes sert, en premier lieu, à développer la technique de la main gauche. L'exercice du legato est justement le moyen le plus apte de contrôler l'inaudibilité des changements de position et des passages de cordes.

5. Bevor mit „dynamischen Nuancen" begonnen wird, empfehle ich, für geraume Zeit mit kräftigem Fingerdruck der linken Hand nur pianissimo zu üben, damit die notwendige Unabhängigkeit der beiden Hände trainiert wird und die allzu oft vorkommende Gleichschaltung (Fingerdruck nur im Forte und zu geringer Fingerdruck im Piano) vermieden wird. Recht oft ist die Kraftanwendung beider Hände automatisch gleichgeschaltet, was wegen zu geringem Fingerdruck der linken Hand zu unschöner Tonqualität führt. Darüber hinaus ist bei vielen Geigern ein merkwürdiger psychologischer Vorgang zu beobachten, indem im Pianissimo die Konzentrationsfähigkeit, also bewußtes Üben gesteigert wird. Die angegebenen Beispiele der Dynamik sollten späterhin weitestgehend ausgebaut werden, so z. B. das Piano Subito, das Forte Subito, der Schweller < >oder auch > < etc.

6. Hinsichtlich der Flageoletts hat sich herausgestellt, daß die Unfähigkeit, Doppelflageoletts wirklich erfolgreich auszuführen, daher stammt, daß bei Flesch ausschließlich der Quartengriff in homophonen Flageoletts vorkommt. Ich habe daher schon bei homophoner Anwendung kleine und große Terzengriffe wie auch Quartengriffe mit ähnlichen Fingersätzen wie bei Fingersatzoktaven und Quintengriffen angegeben.

7. Die deutschen Abkürzungen Sp. – M. – Fr. – G. B. – H. B., die Flesch verwendet, habe ich wie in meinen anderen Publikationen in graphischer Notation dargestellt: ⊏══⊐ ganzer Bogen, ⊏══| Obere Hälfte, |══⊐ Untere Hälfte, ⊏═ Spitze, ≍ Mitte, ⊏⊐ Frosch.

Übungsmethoden für das Skalensystem

1. Zuerst und für geraume Zeit ohne die von Flesch angegebenen variierenden Stricharten üben, also ausschließlich gebunden, um gute unhörbare Lagen- und Saitenwechsel ohne Hilfe der tarnenden Bogenwechsel zu erzielen. Anfänglich ganz langsam je zwei Noten gebunden arbeiten und zwar so, daß jede zweimal gespielt und zur nächsten gebunden wird. Nach und nach bei vorsichtiger Beschleunigung Bindungen bis zur Dauer eines Vierteltaktes, dann zweier Vierteltakte usw. steigern.

2. Für den auf jeder Saite separat notierten einoktavigen Teil Nr. 1 bis 4 sollte man beim Üben zuerst jene Saite wählen, welche mit der tiefsten Lage beginnt. Nach und nach die nächstliegende höhere Lage. Mit anderen Worten: nicht immer mit G-Saite oder in der gedruckten Folge beginnen.

3. Bei allen Moll-Tonarten abwechselnd melodisch oder harmonisch getrennt anwenden.

4. Jede chromatische Skala in Terzen zuerst nur mit statischem Fingersatz ⅓ oder ²⁄₄ üben. Ebenfalls Oktaven mit ¼ oder ⅓.

V. Before the student begins with "dynamic nuances", I recommend practising only pianissimo for some time, with strong finger pressure of the left hand in order to develop the necessary independence of both hands and thus to avoid the all-too-common phenomenon of left hand pressure being applied by the fingers only in forte and too little pressure in piano. Quite often both hands automatically apply (or release) pressure simultaneously, a fact that leads to a disagreeable tonal quality because the pressure exerted by the left fingers is reduced. Moreover, many violinists are subject to the peculiar psychological process that their concentration, i. e., their conscious practising, is increased by pianissimo playing. The given examples of dynamics should later be developed to the fullest to include piano subito, forte subito, the swell < > or > < etc.

VI. Because in single harmonics Flesch uses only the normal position in fourths, students of this method are unable to play double harmonics very successfully. Therefore, I have added minor and major thirds in single harmonics as well as fourths with fingerings similar to those used for the fingered octaves and fifths.

VII. As in my other publications, I have used graphic notation to convey the German abbreviations Sp., M., Fr., G. B., and H. B., used by Flesch: ⊏══⊐ whole Bow, ⊏══| upper half, |══⊐ lower half, ⊏═ ´ tip of bow, ≍ middle, ⊏⊐ nut.

Methods of Practising the Scale System

1. Initially and for a considerable time thereafter, practising should be done without the varying bowings mentioned by Flesch: that is exclusively legato in order to obtain good, inaudible shifts and string crossings without the help of a camouflaging bow change. To begin with, two notes should be played very slowly in succession, each twice and slurred to the next. With gradual, careful acceleration, slurs should be used up to the duration of a quarter note, then to two quarter notes, etc.

2. For the one-octave parts, numbers 1 to 4, printed separately for each string, one should begin practising on the string that starts in the lowest position and gradually work up to the next higher position. In other words, do not always begin with the G string or in the printed sequence.

3. With all minor keys, melodic and harmonics scales should be practised separately in alternating manner.

4. Each chromatic scale in thirds should be played first with static fingerings, namely with ⅓ or ²⁄₄. Also octaves to be fingered ¼ or ⅓ to start with.

V⁰ Avant que l'on s'exerce aux «nuances dynamiques», je conseille d'entraîner le pianissimo avec une forte pression des doigts de la main gauche afin d'atteindre l'indépendance si nécessaire des deux mains et d'en éviter les pressions égales (pression des doigts seulement lorsque l'on joue forte, pression trop réduite lorsque l'on joue piano). Trop souvent, les forces des deux mains ne s'exercent pas indépendamment. Il en résulte, à cause de la pression réduite de la main gauche, une qualité de son insatisfaisante. De plus – phénomène psychologique curieux –, le fait de jouer pianissimo augmente chez beaucoup de violonistes la capacité de concentration, intensifie donc les exercices. Ce ne sera plus tard que l'on devra développer, le plus largement possible, les nuances d'intensité indiquées, telles que piano subito, forte subito, crescendo-decrescendo et decrescendo-crescendo, etc.

VI⁰ En ce qui concerne les harmoniques, il s'est avéré que l'incapacité de réussir les harmoniques doubles découle du fait, que Flesch se limite aux exercices de quartes doigtées ¼. Pour cette raison, j'ai ajouté, même dans les passages homophones, des tierces mineures et majeures, des quartes doigtées comme les octaves doigtées et des quintes.

VII⁰ J'ai représenté les abréviations Sp., M., G. B., H. B., employées par Flesch, par les mêmes signes graphiques que dans mes autres publications: ⊏══⊐ tout l'archet, ⊏══| moitié supérieure, |══⊐ moitié inférieure, ⊏═ pointe, ≍ milieu, ⊏⊐ talon.

Méthodes d'entraînement pour le système de gammes

1⁰ D'abord et pour un certain temps, s'abstenir des variations indiquées par Flesch pour les coups d'archet, donc s'exercer exclusivement en liant les notes afin de bien réussir de bons et inaudibles changements de position et passages de cordes, sans l'effet camouflant causé par un changement du coup d'archet. Au début, travailler très lentement en liant deux notes de sorte que chaque note soit jouée deux fois et lors de sa répétition liée à la suivante. Accélérer doucement pour arriver à des liaisons pour la durée d'une noire, de deux noires, etc.

2⁰ Pour les passages comprenant une octave seulement (numéros 1 à 4), notés séparément pour chaque corde, travailler d'abord la corde qui commence par la position la plus basse. Passer lentement à la prochaine position plus élevée. Autrement dit, ne pas toujours commencer par la corde de sol ni dans l'ordre indiqué dans l'édition.

3⁰ Pour toutes les gammes mineures faire alterner mélodique et harmonique séparément.

4⁰ Commencer l'exercice des gammes chromatiques en tierces par les doigtés statiques ⅓ ou ²⁄₄, et en octaves par ¼ ou ⅓.

5. Pizzicati können nach Belieben verändert und erweitert werden.

6. Das Skalensystem in seiner Urform war bereits so umfangreich, daß die meisten Geiger – selbst bei Beschränkung auf eine einzige Tonart – nicht das gesamte Material an einem Tag bewältigen konnten, wenn noch daneben Etüden, Bogenübungen und Repertoire zu ihrem Übungsprogramm gehörten. Durch meine zusätzlichen Vorschläge müßte man wohl, wenn man nicht rationell vorgeht, wesentlich mehr Zeit dafür ansetzen. Ich mache daher einige Vorschläge, um diesem Dilemma abzuhelfen, die aber je nach Bedürfnis und Geschmack abgewandelt werden können.

1. Tag: Homophone Skalen, Nr. 1 bis 4, mit meinen Erweiterungen, Terzen, Normaloktaven, Dezimen mit meinen Ergänzungen, Flageoletts im Quartgriff mit 1. und 4. Finger.

2. Tag: Dreioktavige homophone Skalen, Nr. 5 mit meinem Ergänzungen, Primen, Quarten, Sexten, Normaloktaven mit Ergänzungen.

3. Tag: Ganztonleiter, Quinten, Normaloktaven, Fingersatzoktaven, Flageoletts im Quartintervall, aber diesmal mit $1/3$ und $2/4$.

4. Tag: Wieder homophone Skalen, Nr. 1 bis 4, Vierteltonleiter, Normaloktaven, Flageoletts im Quintengriff, und linke Hand Pizzicati.

5. Tag: Wieder dreioktavige homophone Skalen Nr. 5, Quinten, Septimen, Normaloktaven, Fingersatzoktaven, Flageoletts im großen Terzgriff.

6. Tag: Ganztonleiter, Primen, Quinten, Normaloktaven, Flageoletts im kleinen Terzgriff, Pizzicati.

7. Tag: Sonntag: Dreioktavige homophone Skalen Nr. 5, Terzen, Quinten, Normaloktaven.

Bei dieser Einteilung wird ersichtlich, daß gewisse Teile nur einmal pro Woche drankommen, andere, etwas wichtigere zwei bis dreimal und Normaloktaven täglich, da die Quartlage für die Intonation von größter Bedeutung ist.
Die von mir vorgeschlagene Reihenfolge und Rekapitulation kann je nach Bedürfnis abgewandelt werden, und ich zitiere nochmals Carl Flesch, der in der Fußnote der ersten Seite seines Vorwortes „nicht eine starre unelastische Übungsart" empfiehlt.
In neuester Zeit, also in den achtziger Jahren des 20. Jahrhunderts, werden Zweifel über den Sinn und die Notwendigkeit des Übens von Skalen geäußert, was offenbar zum Teil auf Originalitätssucht und auf mangelnder Kenntnis der Materie beruht. Schließlich waren diese Übungen vielen Generationen von bedeutenden Geigern von großem Nutzen. So ist z. B. Heifetz überzeugt davon, und er stellt die Forderung des Übens von Skalen nicht nur an seine Schüler, sondern ebenso an sich selbst.

---

5. Pizzicati can be varied and extended at will.

6. The Scale System in its original edition is already so voluminous that most violinist, even when confining themselves to a single key, cannot manage the entire material in one day if they also intend to practise études, bowing exercices, and repertoire. My additional suggestions could lead to one's spending even more time with the scale system unless one proceeds in a rational manner. The following advice, as one's needs and taste dictate, is given to resolve this problem.

1st day: Homophonic scales Numbers 1 to 4, with my extensions, thirds, normal octaves, tenths with my supplements, normal harmonics fingered $1/4$.

2nd day: Three-octave homophonic scales Number 5, with my additions, unisons, fourths, sixth, normal octaves with my supplements.

3rd day: Whole-tone scale, fifths, normal octaves, fingered octaves, harmonics in fourths interval, but this time fingered $1/3$ and $2/4$.

4th day: Again homophonic scales, Numbers 1 to 4, quarter-tone scale, normal octaves, harmonics in fifths interval and left hand pizzicati.

5th day: Again three-octave homophonic scales Number 5, fifths, sevenths, normal octaves, fingered octaves, harmonics in major thirds.

6th day: Whole-tone scale, unisons, fifths, normal octaves, harmonics in minor thirds, pizzicati.

7th day: Sunday: Three-octave homophonic scales Number 5, thirds, fifths, normal octaves.

This schedule makes it evident that certain parts are practised once a week only, other somewhat more important ones two to three times, and normal octaves daily, as the normal distance of 1st to 4th finger in the interval of a fourth is of great significance for the intonation.
The proposed sequence and recapitulation can be changed as required, and I am quoting Carl Flesch again, who in the footnote on the first page of his preface, recommends "not by any means a rigid unelastic method of practising".
In recent times, meaning the 1980s, there have been doubts as to the purpose and necessity of practising scales, a view stemming partly from an addiction to originality and a lack of insight. After all, those exercices were of great advantage for generations of outstanding violinists. Heifetz, for instance, is convinced of their usefulness, and he requires of his students as much as of himself that scales be practised.

5⁰ Modifier et étendre les pizzicati à volonté.

6⁰ Déjà dans sa forme initiale, le système de gammes était trop vaste pour être exécuté, chaque jour, même en se limitant à une seule tonalité, d'un bout à l'autre en outre des études, exercices d'archet et de répertoire. Les suggestions que j'ajoute prolongeraient encore la durée des exercices, à moins que l'on adopte une méthode plus rationnelle. Je fais donc quelques propositions pour sortir de ce dilemme, propositions à modifier aux besoins et au goût:

1er jour: les gammes homophones, numéros 1 à 4, avec mes extensions, tierces avec mes additions, octaves normales avec mes suppléments, dixièmes avec mes suppléments, harmoniques normaux doigtés $1/4$

2e jour: gammes homophones sur trois octaves, numéro 5, avec mes suppléments, unissons, quartes, sextes, octaves normales avec suppléments.

3e jour: gammes de tons entiers quintes, octaves normales, octaves doigtées, harmoniques doigtés $1/3$ et $2/4$.

4e jour: gammes homophones, numéros 1 à 4, gamme en quarts de ton, octaves normales, harmoniques de quinte, pizzicati de la main gauche.

5e jour: gammes homophones sur trois octaves numéro 5, quintes, septièmes, octaves normales, octaves doigtées, harmoniques de tierce majeure.

6e jour: gammes de tons, entiers, unissons, quintes, octaves normales, harmoniques tierce mineure, pizzicati.

7e jour, dimanche: gammes homophones sur trois octaves, numéro 5, tierces, quintes, octaves normales.

Selon cette répartition, certaines parties ne sont exécutées qu'une fois par semaine, d'autres plus importantes, deux ou trois fois, et les octaves normales, tous les jours, vu l'éminente importance des intervalles de quarte pour l'intonation.
L'ordre et la récapitulation que je propose sont à modifier selon les besoins. Je cite encore une fois Carl Flesch qui recommande, dans la note au bas de la première page de sa préface, de ne pas adopter «une manière d'étudier, inexorablement raide et engourdie».
Si tout récemment, c'est-à-dire au cours des années quatre-vingts, on met en cause sens et nécessité des exercices de gammes, ceci est dû apparemment à une recherche maniaque d'originalité et un manque de compétence. En effet, ces exercices ont rendu service à des générations d'interprètes célèbres. Heifetz p.ex. est convaincu de leur valeur et demande à ses élèves de s'y soumettre comme il fait lui-même.

Der Sohn von Ysaÿe schreibt in der Ausgabe „Exercices et Gammes" von Eugène Ysaÿe: „Wir können auch bestätigen, daß diese Übungen und Skalen die Basis von Eugène Ysaÿes eigener technischer Morgen-Gymnastik formten, zu welcher er noch improvisierte Varianten in verblüffender Weise erfand".

Szigeti schreibt in seinem Vorwort zum selben Werk, daß Skalen ein solch unwandelbarer Bestandteil unseres grundlegenden Rüstzeugs seien, daß jedes Skalensystem seinem Vorgänger oder Zeitgenossen gleiche, wenn man es nachlässig und ohne historische Perspektive betrachte.

Übrigens wird die Notwendigkeit von Skalensystemen auch dadurch unterstrichen, daß in den Programmen großer internationaler Violinwettbewerbe wie z. B. den Wettbewerben Yehudi Menuhin, Paris, und Fritz Kreisler, Graz, Skalen verlangt werden.

Max Rostal   Bern, 1986

In the edition "Exercices et gammes" by Eugène Ysaÿe, the author's son writes: "We can also state that these 'Exercices and Scales' formed the basis of Eugène Ysaÿe's own technical gymnastics in the mornings, to which he added improvised variants of dazzling fantasy".

In his preface to the same work Szigeti writes: "Scales are such an immutable basic ingredient of our equipment that any 'scale system' resembles its predecessor or contemporary when one looks at it casually and without historical perspective".

Incidentally, the necessity of scale systems is underlined by the fact that important international violin competitions such as the Yehudi Menuhin Competition in Paris and the Fritz Kreisler Competition in Graz require scales to be performed in their programmes.

Max Rostal   Berne, 1986

Dans l'édition des «Exercices et Gammes» par Eugène Ysaÿe, le fils de l'auteur se prononce à ce sujet: «Nous pouvons d'autre part affirmer que ces 'Exercices et Gammes' constituaient la base de la gymnastique technique matinale d'Eugène Ysaÿe lui-même qui y ajoutait des variantes improvisées d'une éblouissante fantaisie».

Joseph Szigeti désigne, dans la préface de cette même édition, les gammes comme un élément invariable de l'équipement de base étant donné que chaque système de gammes ressemble à ses prédécesseurs et contemporains lorsqu'on le considère superficiellement et sans le placer dans son cadre historique.

D'ailleurs, la nécessité de travailler des systèmes de gammes est soulignée par le fait que, dans les programmes des grands concours internationaux de violon, tels que les concours Yehudi Menuhin à Paris et Fritz Kreisler à Graz, l'exécution de gammes est obligatoire.

Max Rostal   Berne, en 1986

C dur, c major, do majeur, do maggiore, c groote terts.

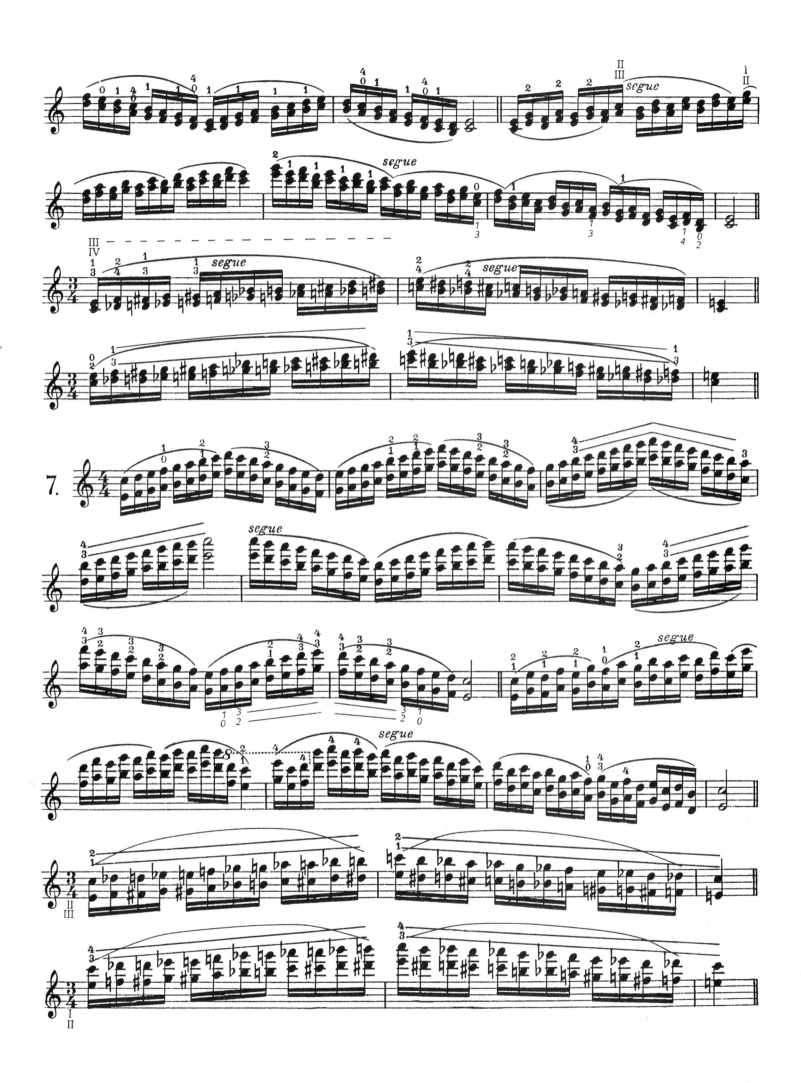

A moll, a minor, la mineur, la minore, a kleine terts.

F dur, f major, fa majeur, fa maggiore, f groote terts.

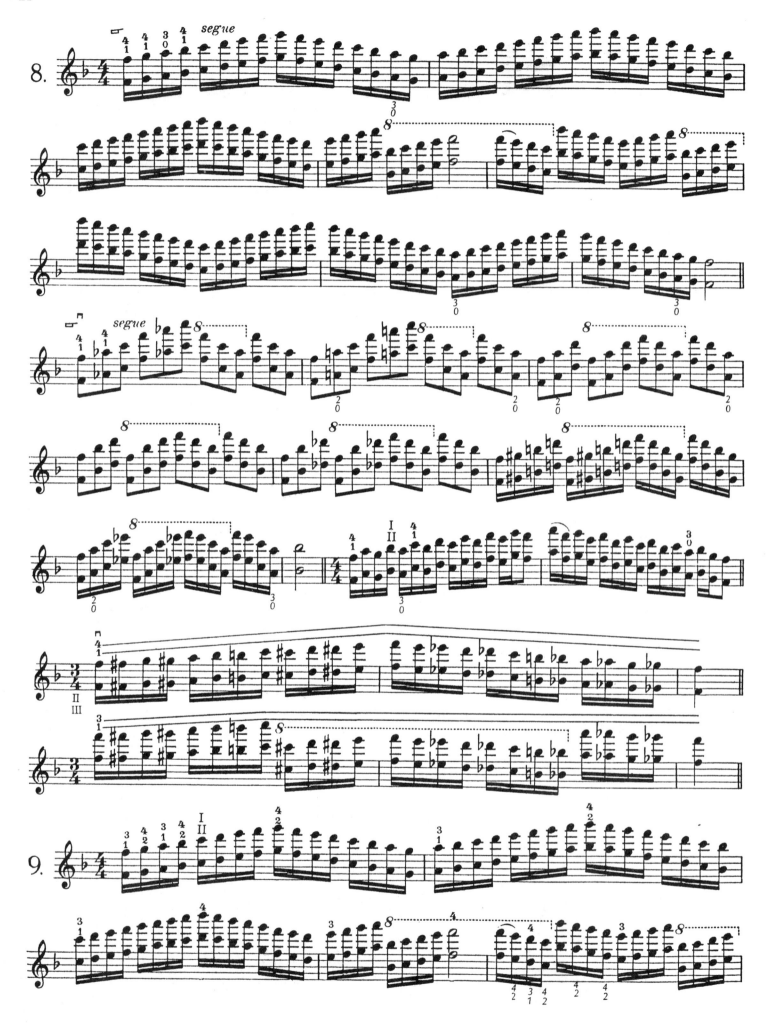

15

D moll, d minor, ré mineur, re minore, d kleine terts.

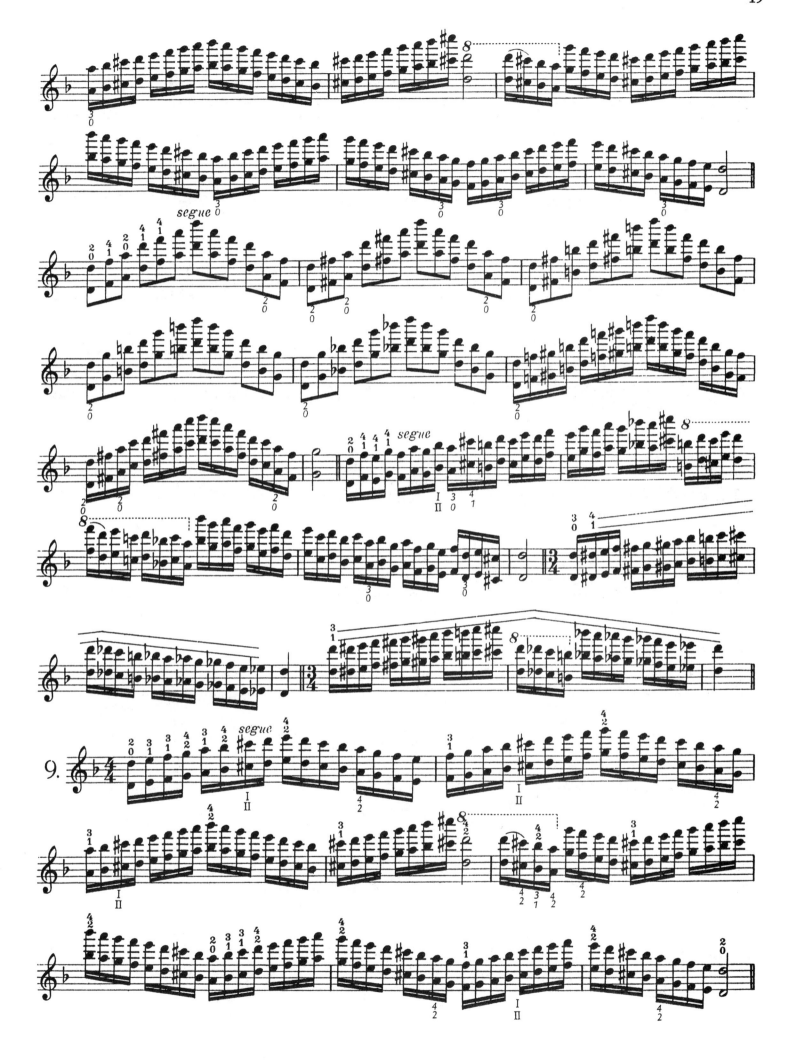

B dur, bb major, sib majeur, sib maggiore, bes groote terts.

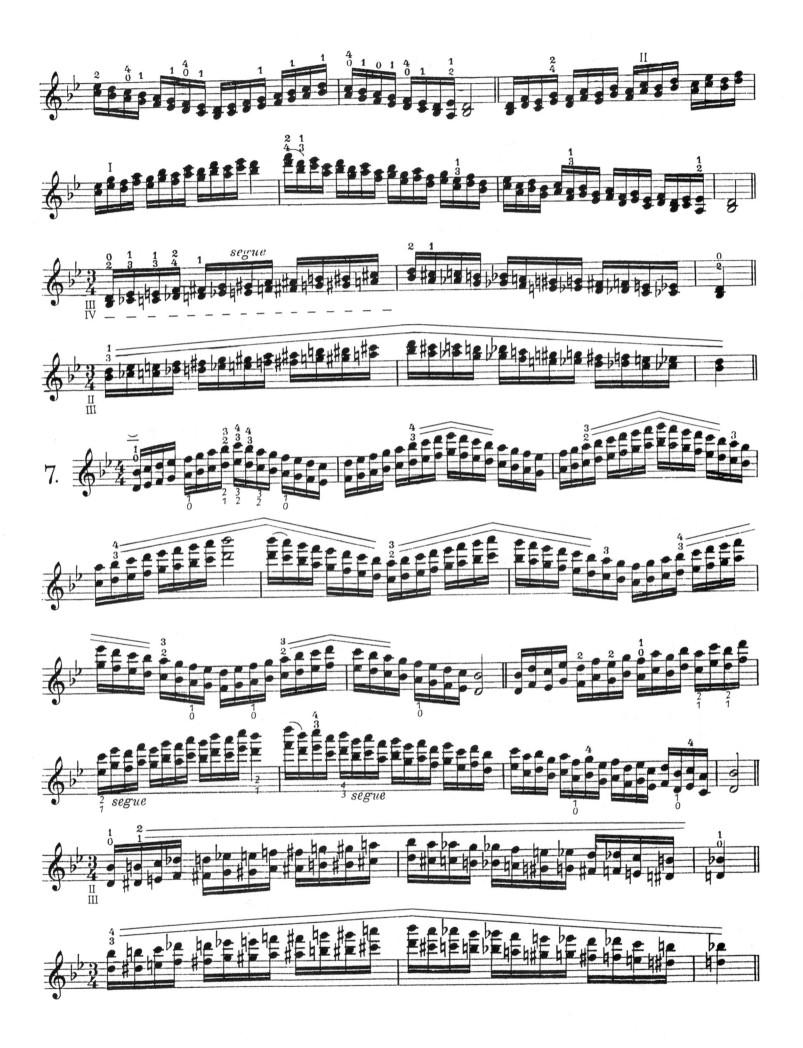

24

G moll, g minor, sol mineur, sol minore, g kleine terts

28

Es dur, eb major, mib majeur, mib maggiore, es groote terts.

C moll, c minor, do mineur, do minore, c kleine terts.

*Bogeneinteilung wie bei Nr. 1.
Bowdivision as in N°. 1.

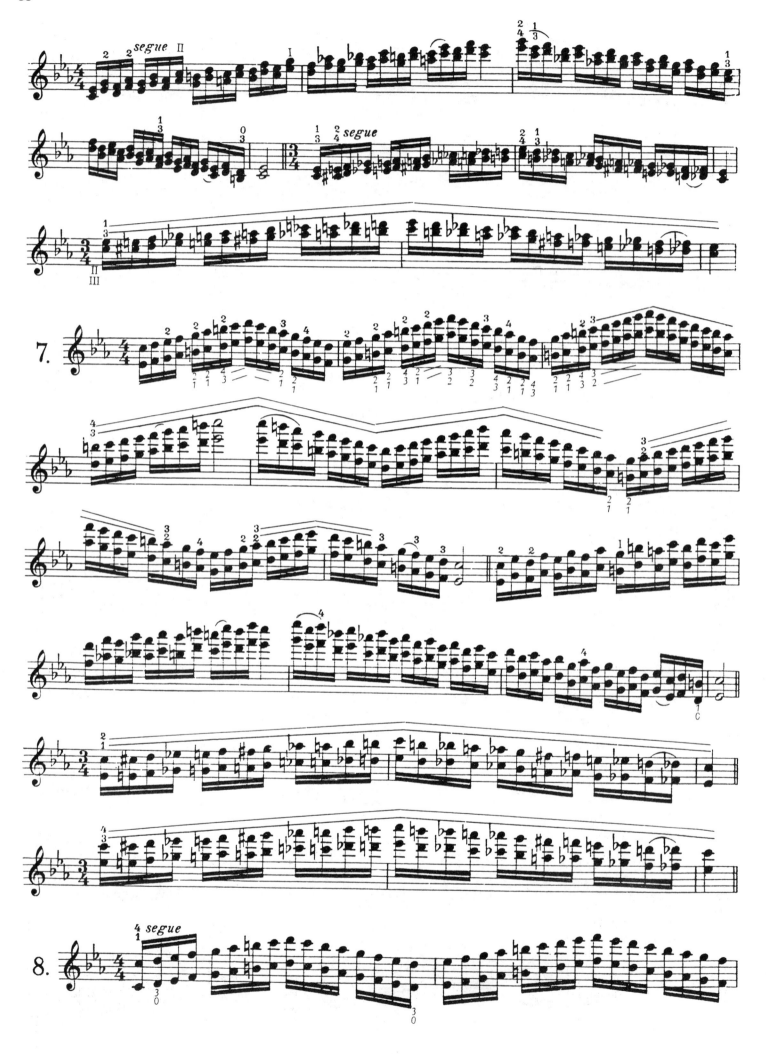

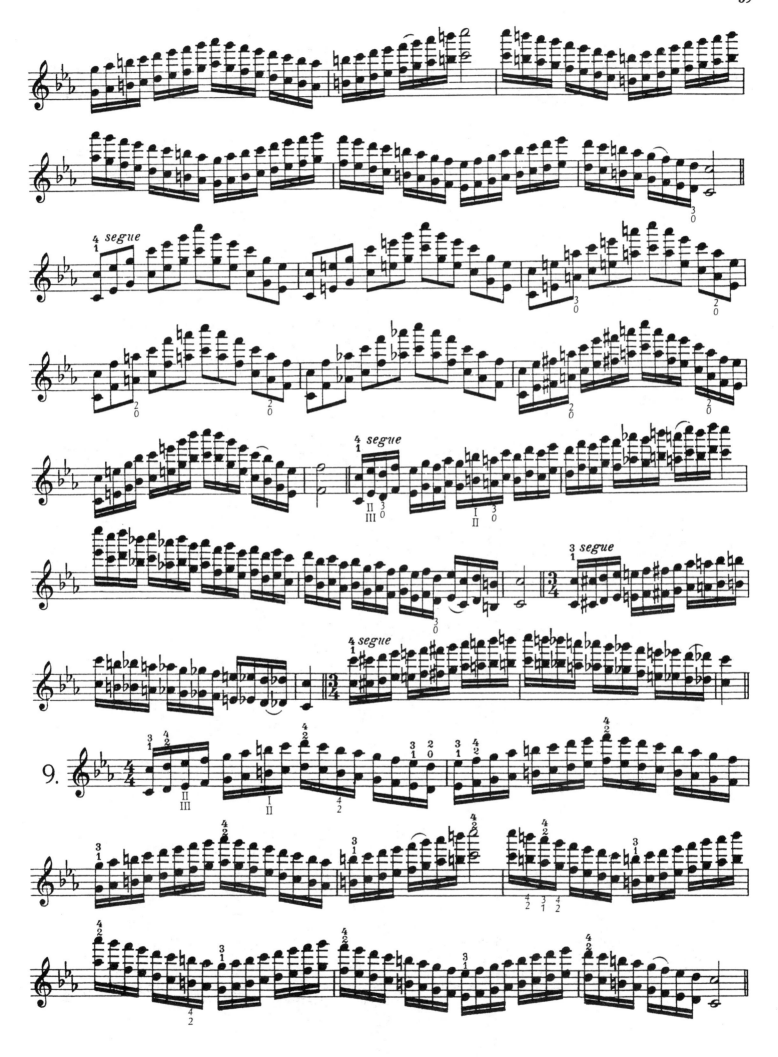

As dur, a♭ major, la♭ majeur, la♭ maggiore, as groote terts.

*Bogeneinteilung wie bei Nr. 1.
Bowdivision as in N°. 1.

42

F moll, f minor, fa mineur, fa minore, f kleine terts.

✻ Bogeneinteilung wie bei Nr. 1/2
Bowdivision as in No. 1/2

Des dur, d♭ major, ré♭ majeur, re♭ maggiore, des groote terts

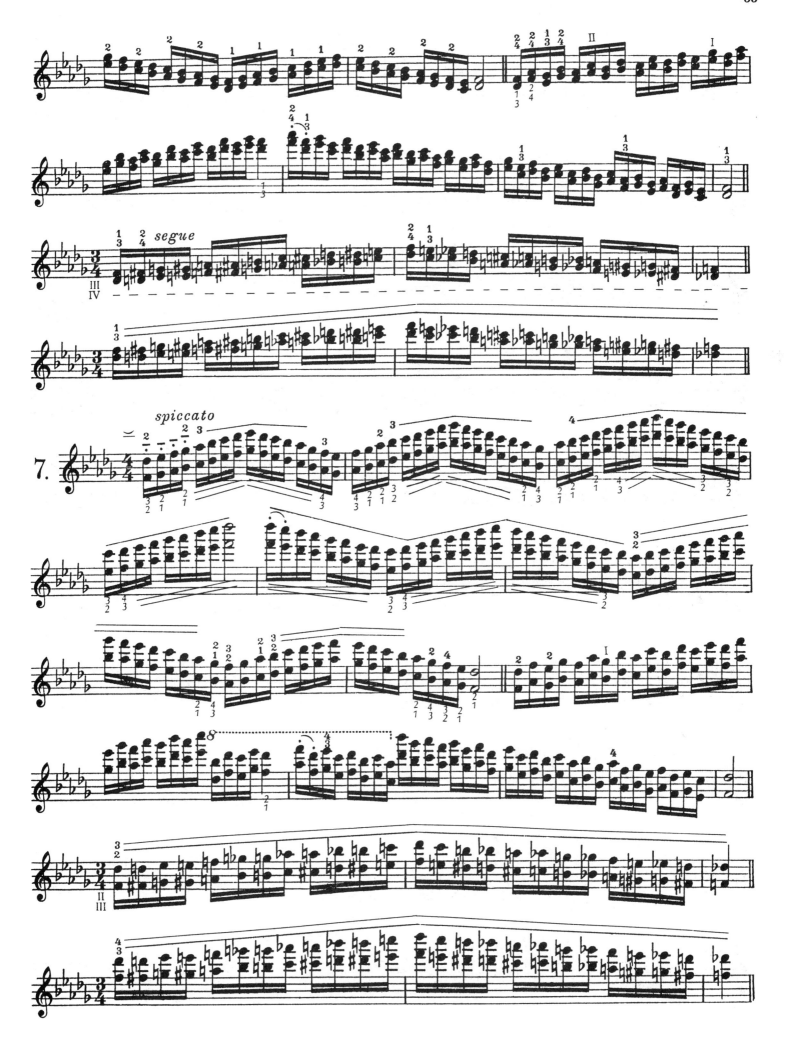

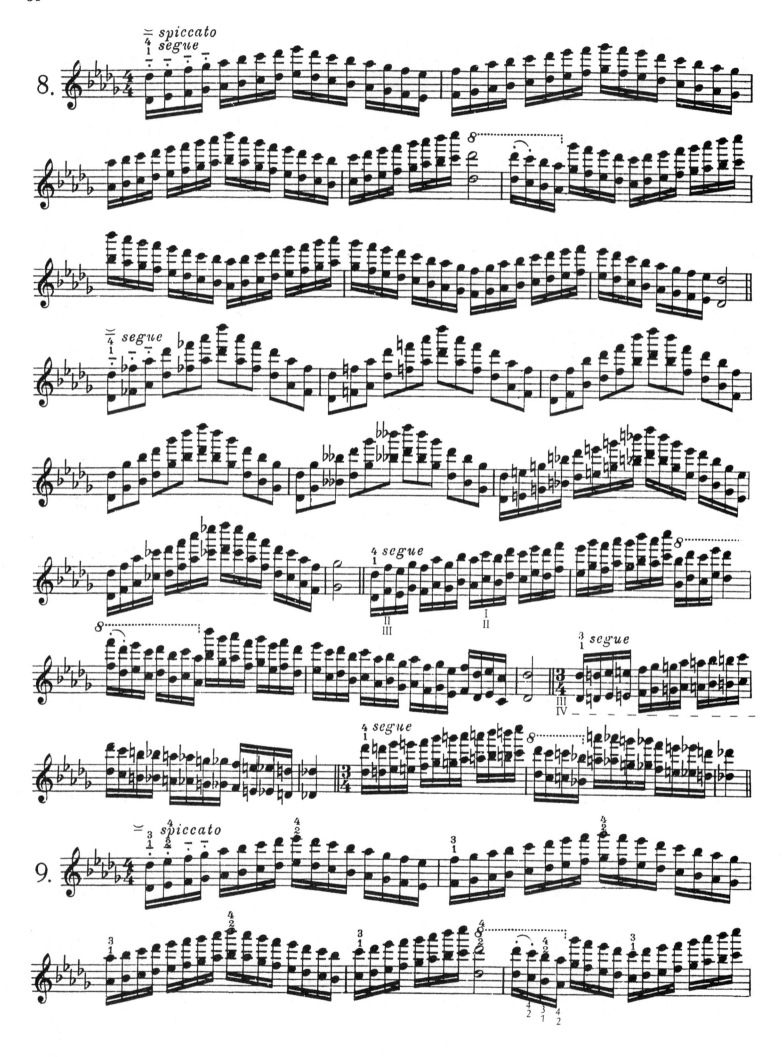

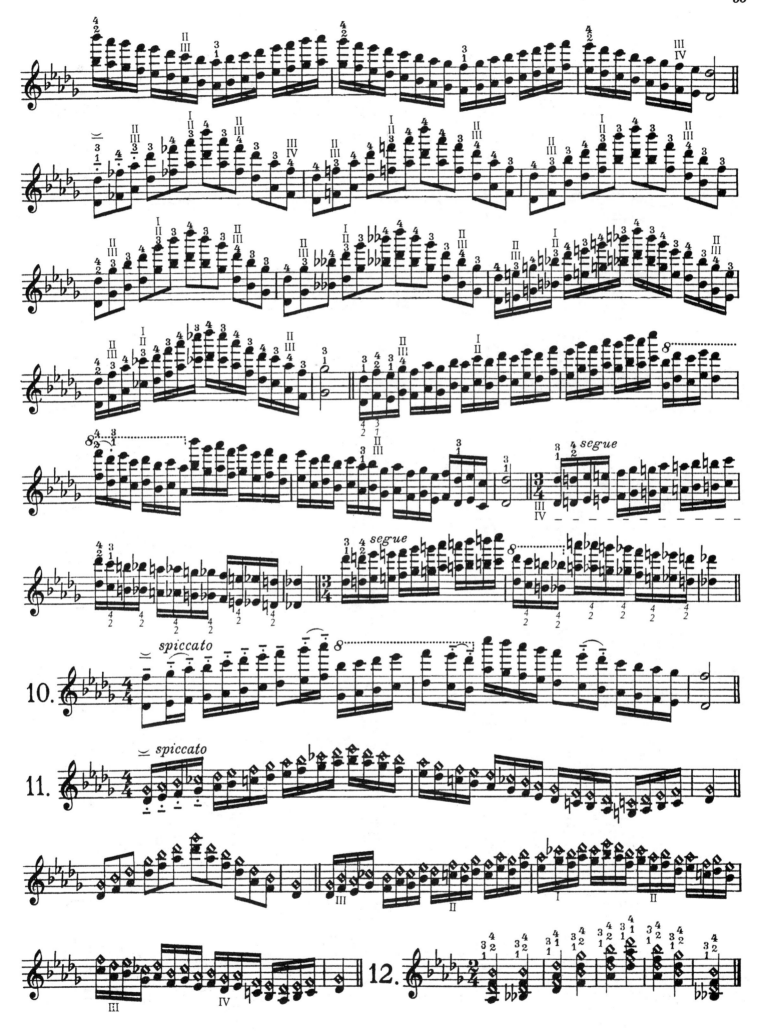

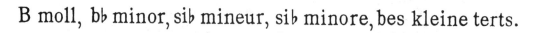

B moll, bb minor, sib mineur, sib minore, bes kleine terts.

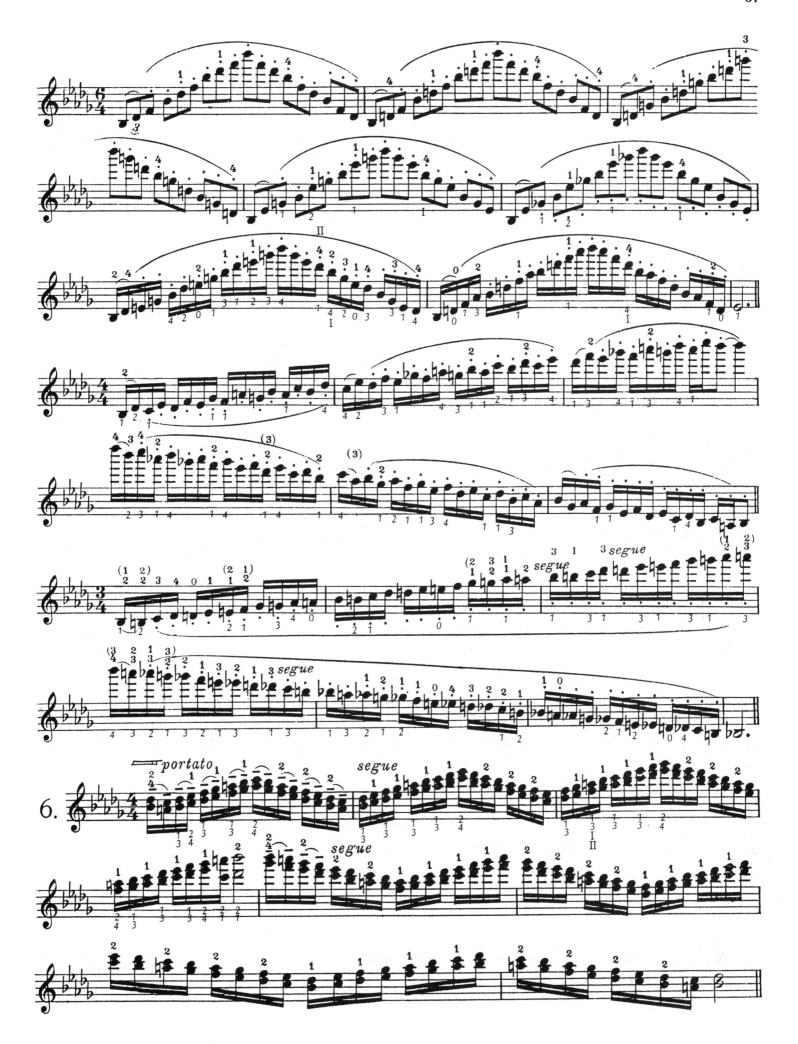

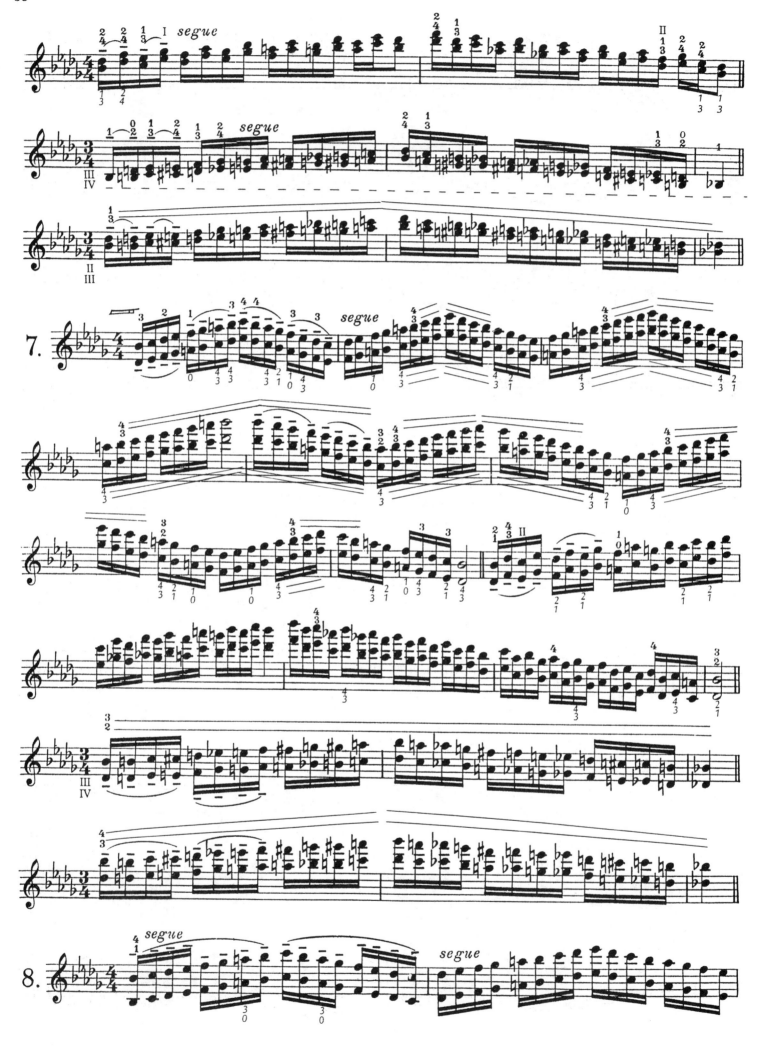

Ges dur, g♭ major, sol♭ majeur, sol♭ maggiore, ges groote terts.

✱ Bogeneinteilung wie bei Nʳ. ½
Bowdivision as in Nº. ½

Es moll, e♭ minor, mi♭ mineur, mi♭ minore, es kleine terts.

※ Bogeneinteilung wie bei N^{r.} ½
Bowdivision as in N^{o.} ½

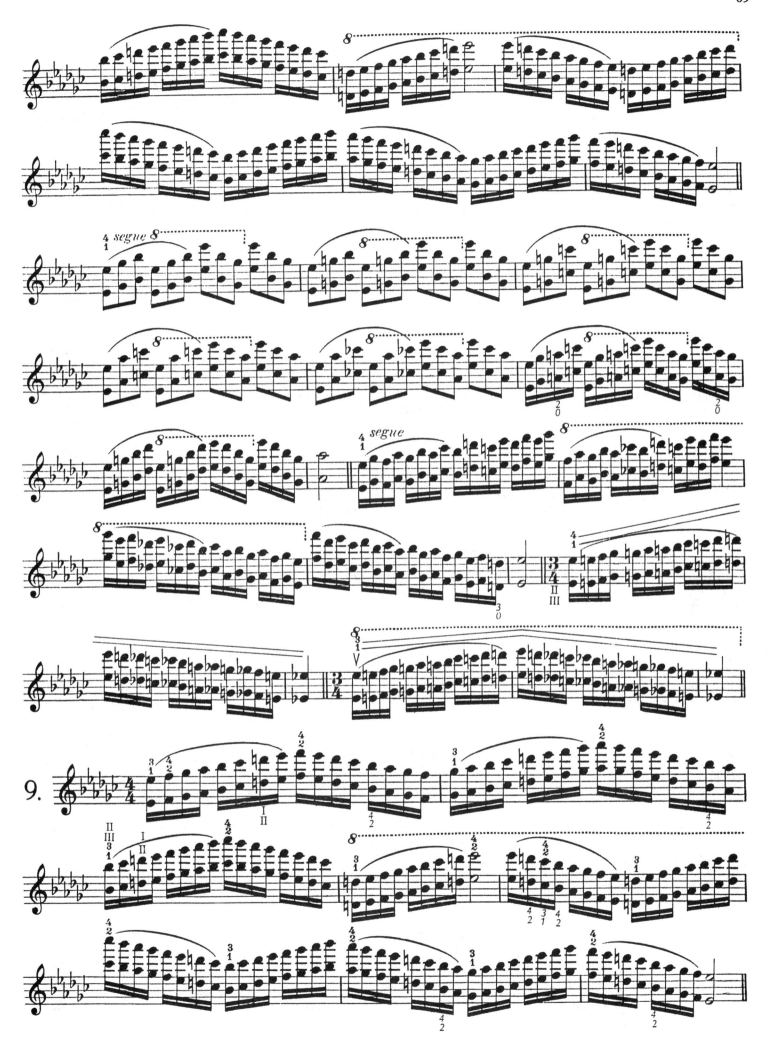

H dur, b major, si majeur, si maggiore, b groote terts.

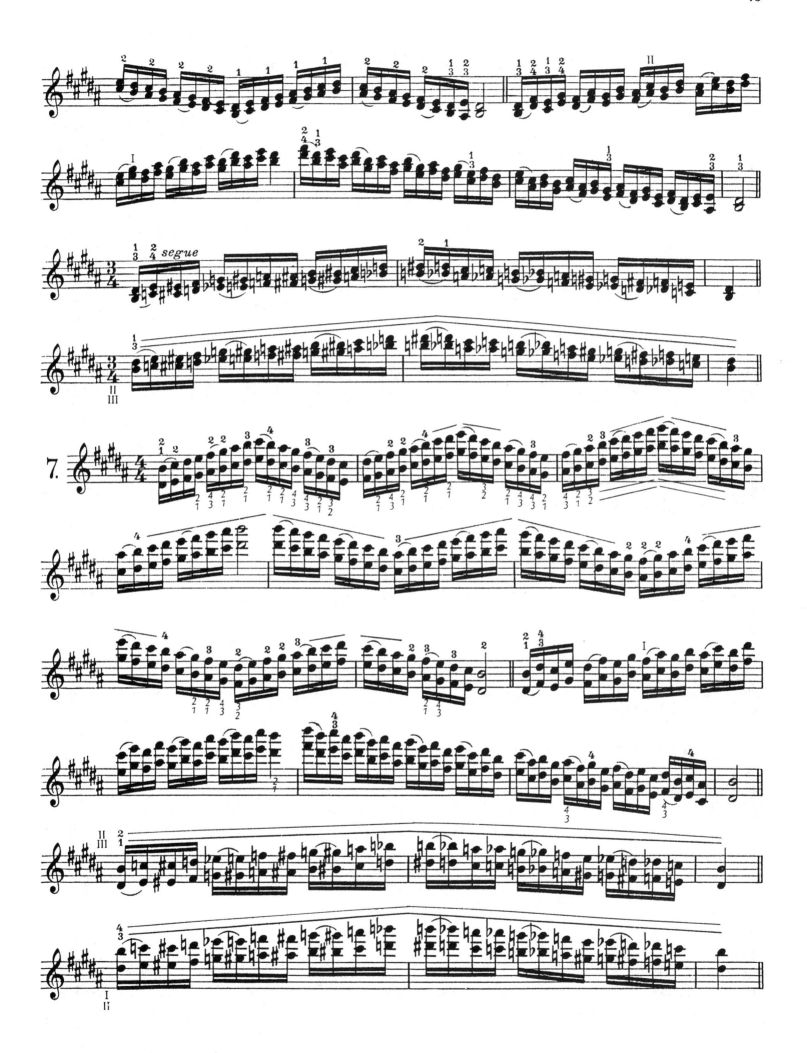

Gis moll, g♯ minor, sol♯ mineur, sol♯ minore, gis kleine terts.

✣ Bogeneinteilung wie bei N^r. 1.
Bowdivision as in N°. 1.

E dur, e major, mi majeur, mi maggiore, e groote terts.

∴ Bogeneinteilung wie bei Nr. ½
Bowdivision as in No. ½

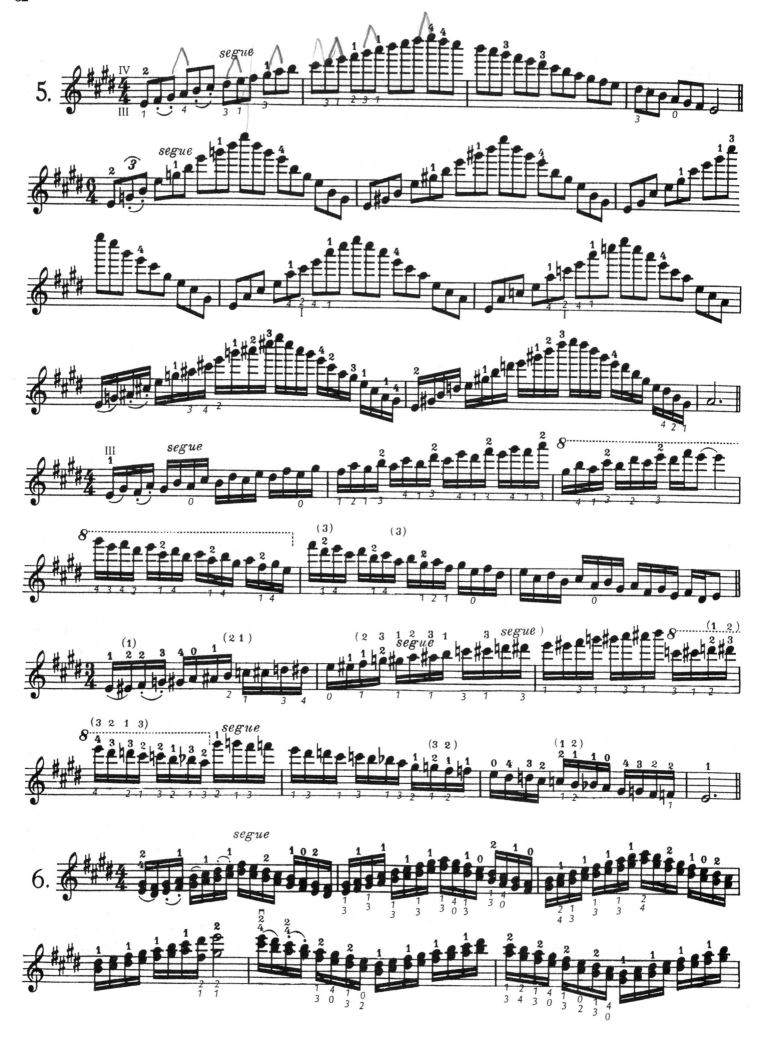

85

Cis moll, c♯ minor, do♯ mineur, do♯ minore, cis kleine terts.

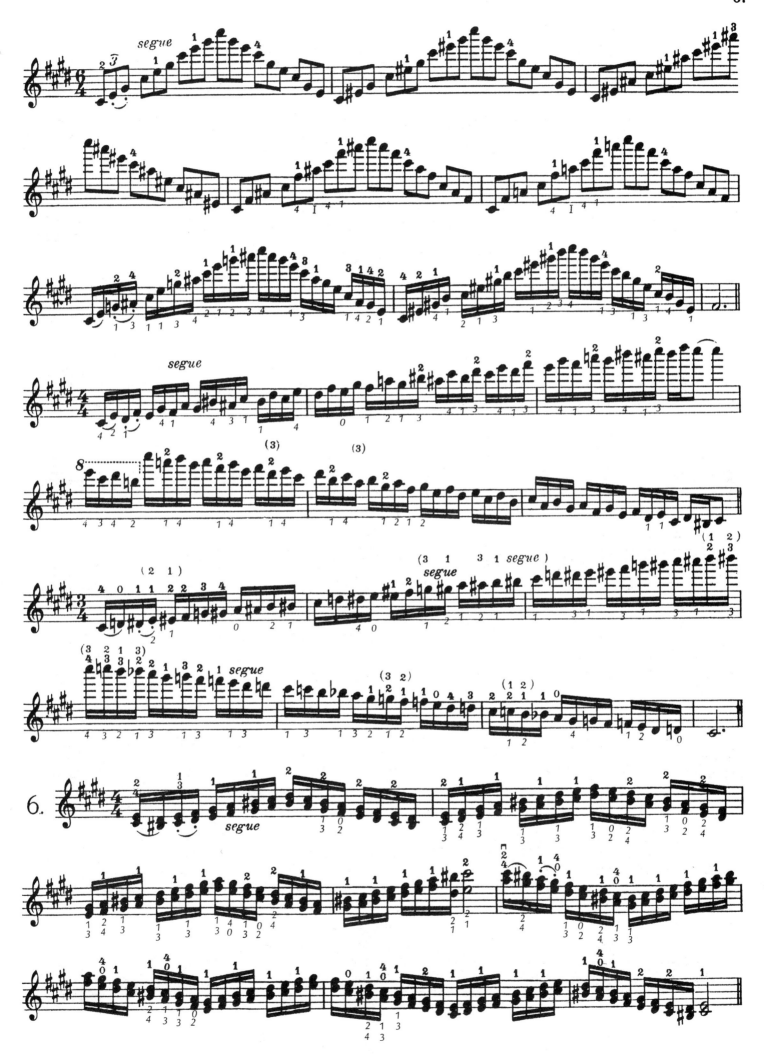

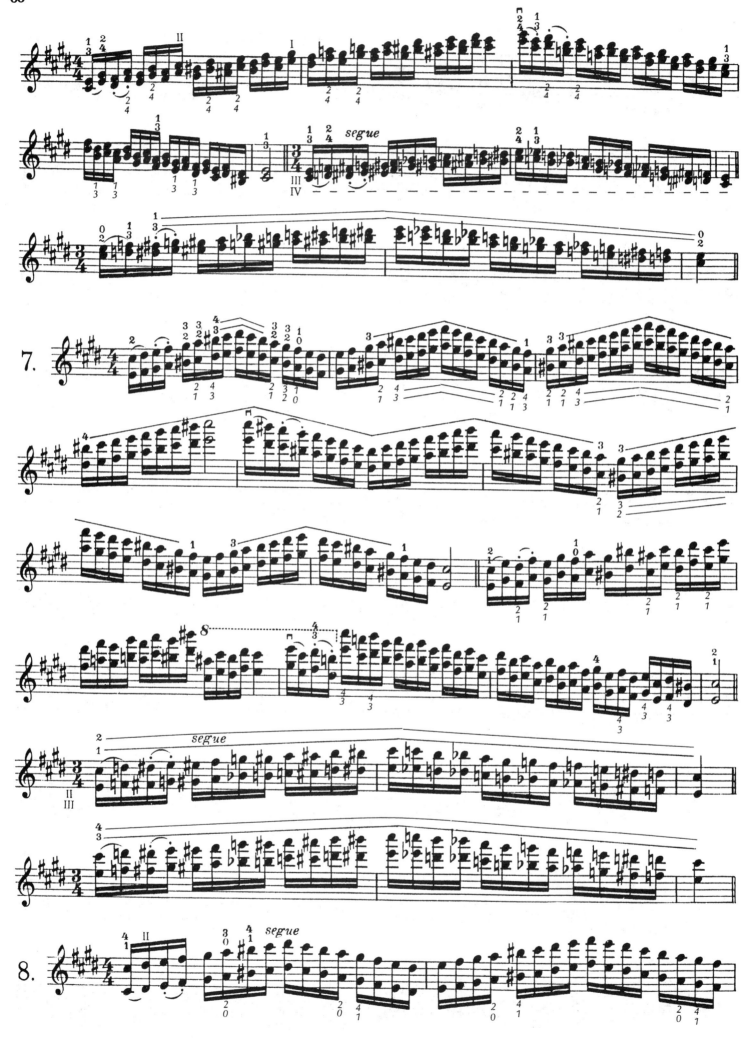

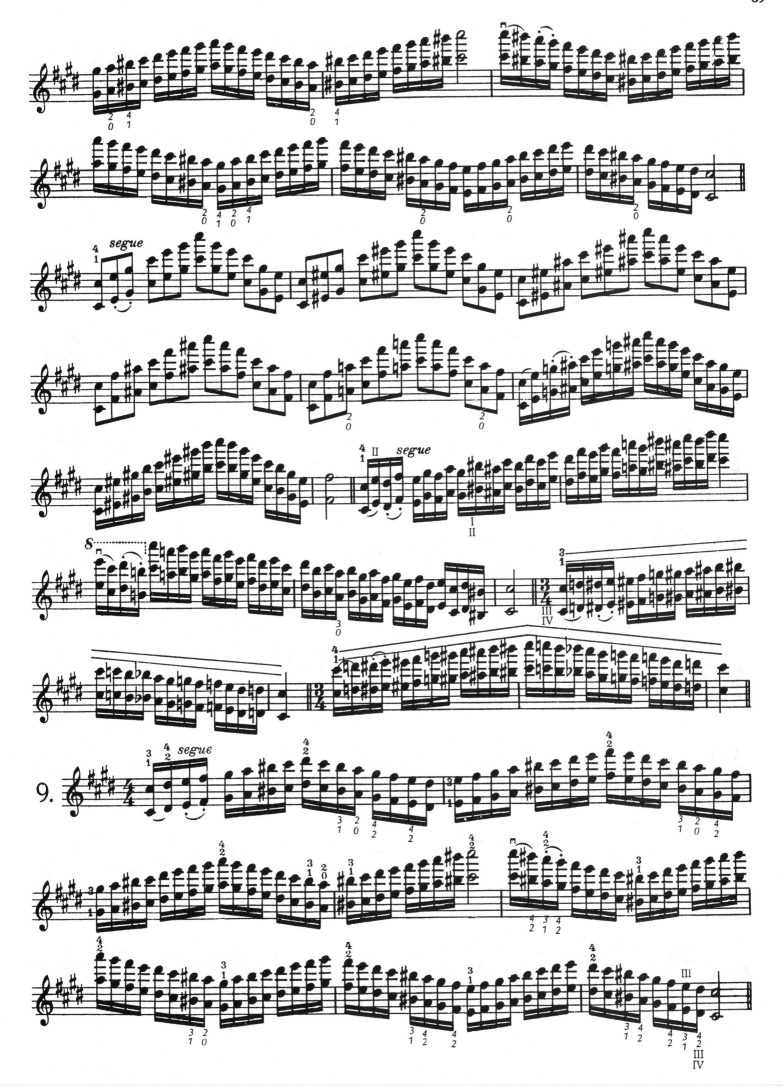

A dur, a major, la majeur, la maggiore, a groote terts.

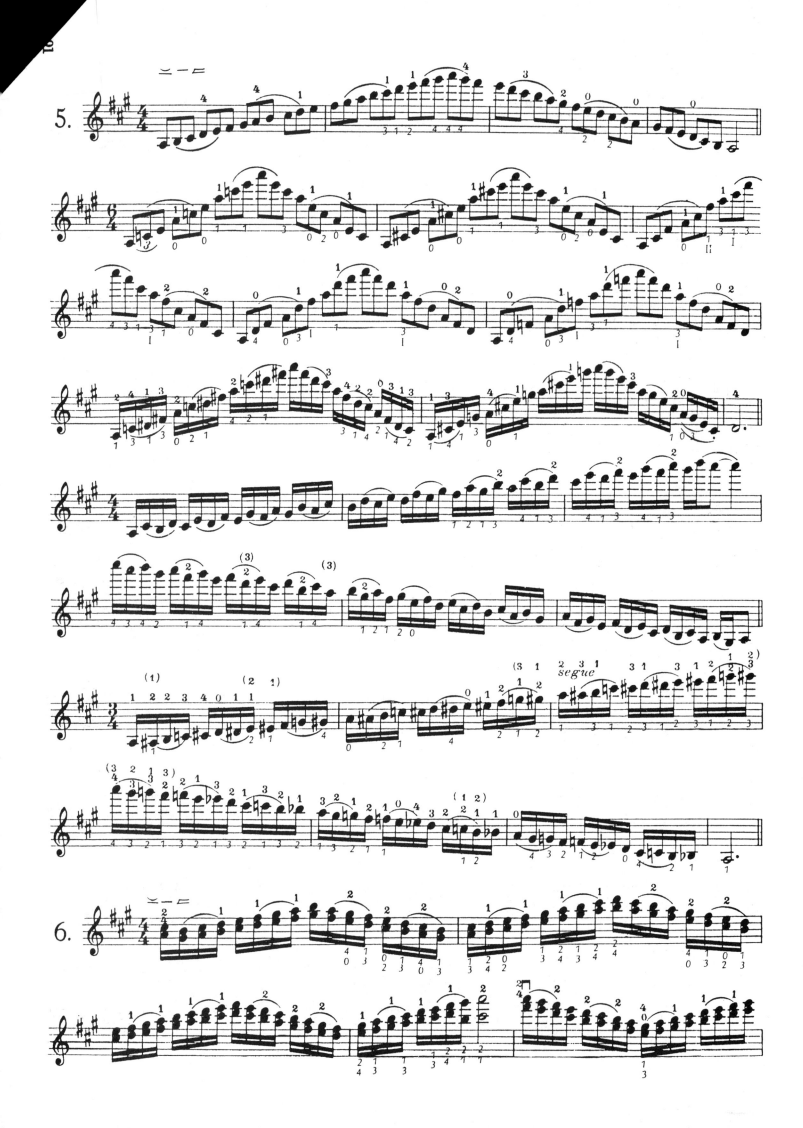

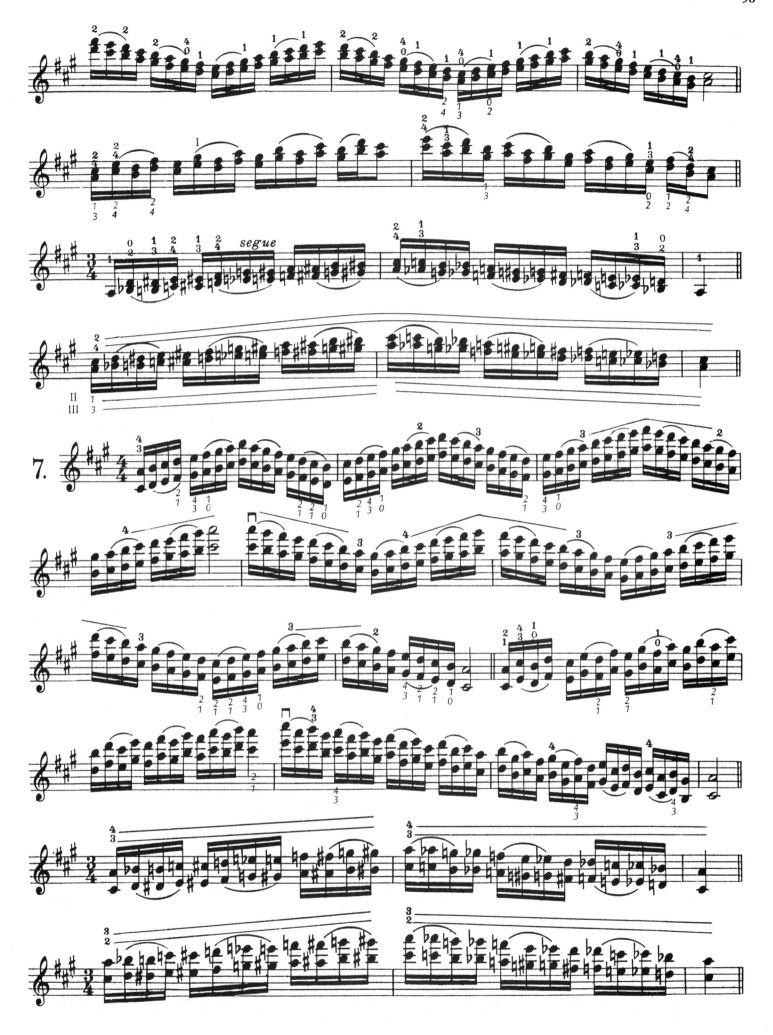